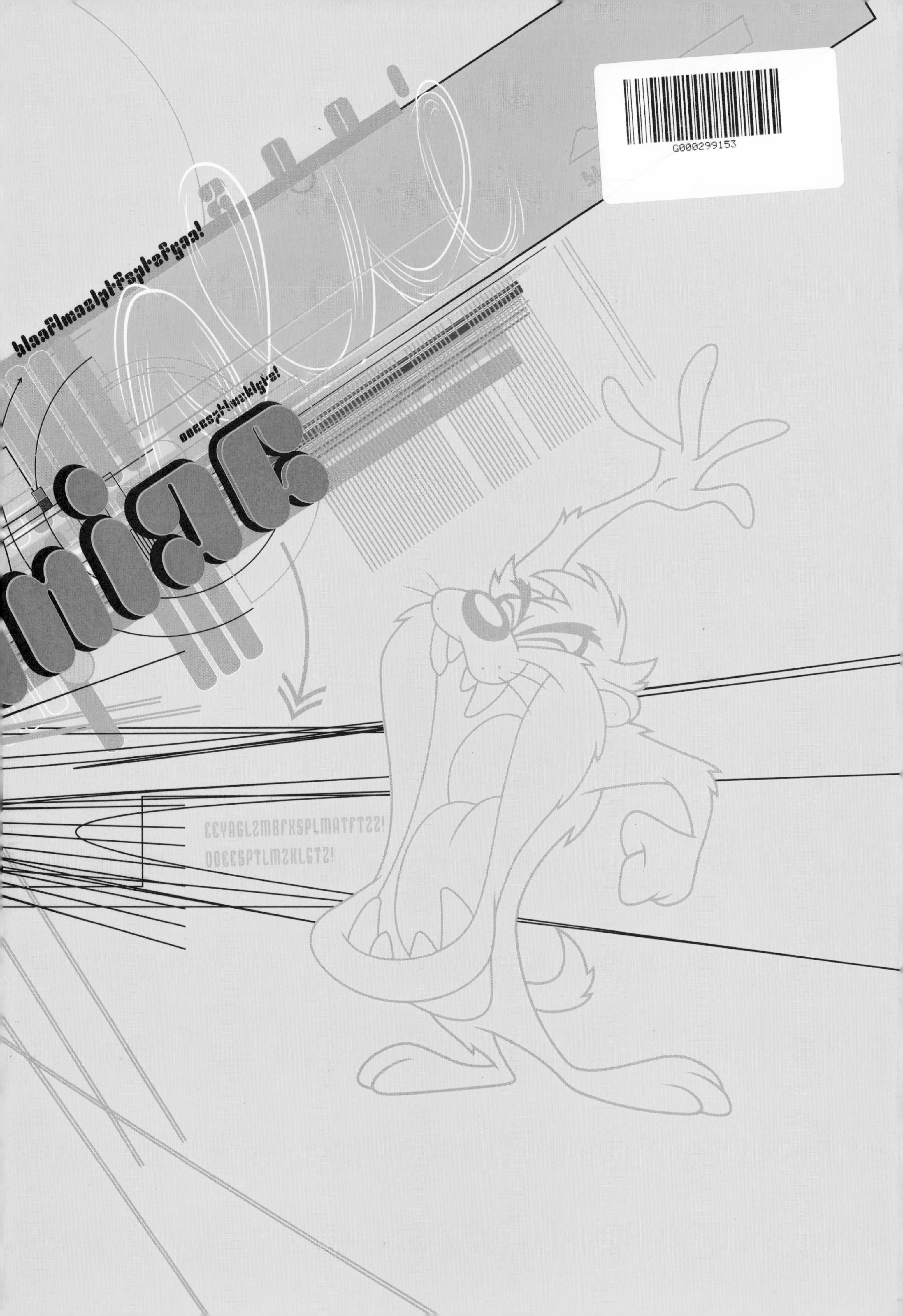

CONTENTS

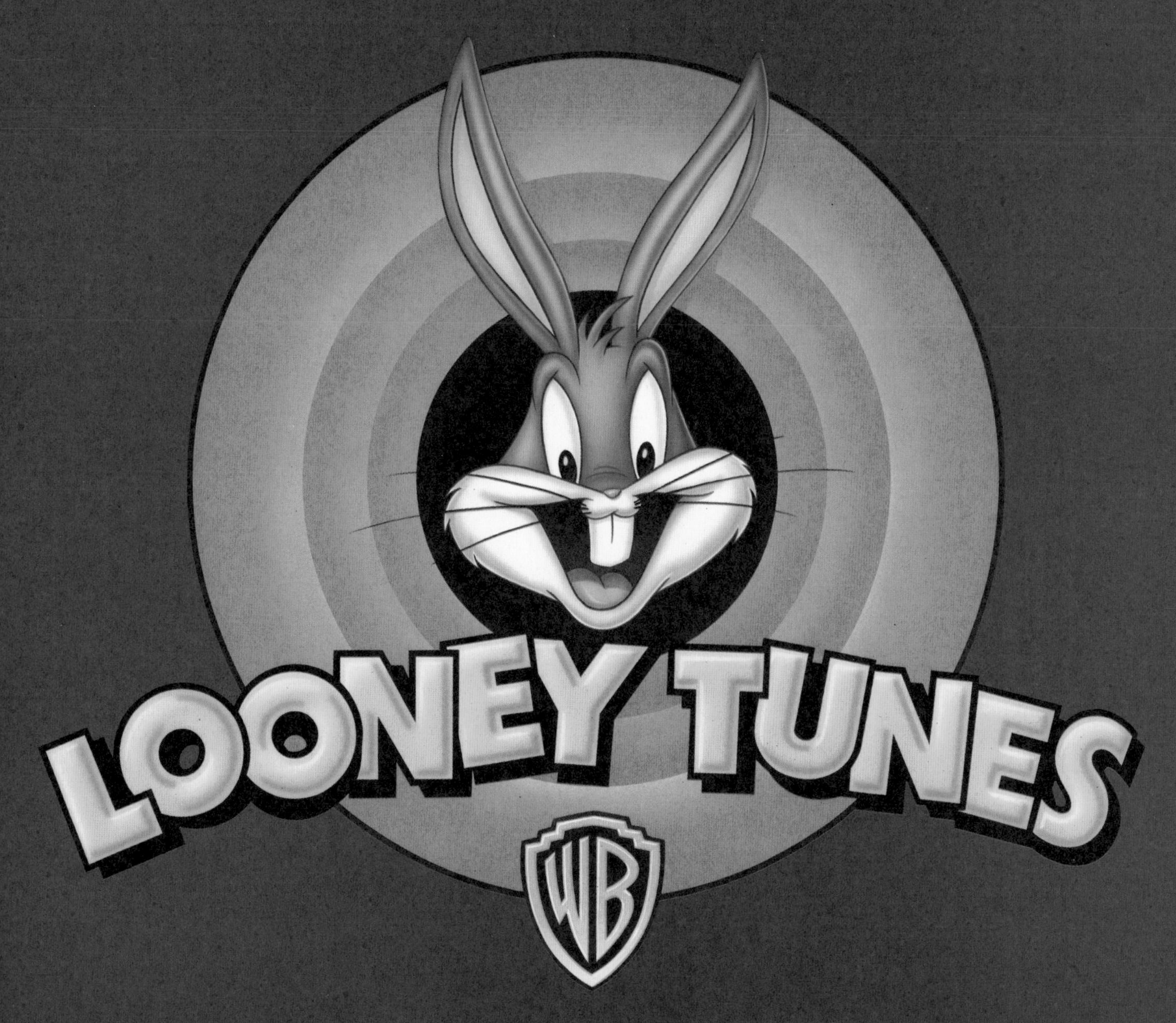

ANNUAL 2001

Pedigree®

Published by Pedigree Books Limited
The Old Rectory, Matford Lane, Exeter, EX2 4PS

£6.99

GOOD EVENING, SKATING FANS! THIS IS CRASH O'MALLEY AT RINGSIDE COVERING TONIGHT'S ROLLER DERBY ACTION!
THE TRADITIONAL RIVALRY CONTINUES, AS THE ALTOONA ARM-BREAKERS FACE THE WALLA WALLA WIPEOUTS HERE AT...
ROLLER DERBY
BOX OFFICE
GO!
90210
WB1767
PISMO BEACH! AT LAST!
HOLD ON, DOC! THIS DON'T LOOK LIKE PISMO BEACH TO ME! NO SURFERS, NO TANNING SALON, NO BEACH BUNNIES ...?
ROLL OUT THE BUNNY
AND HERE SHE COMES! #36-21-36-- QUEENIE, THE BOMBSHELL BUNNY!
AI-YI-YI!!
DON'T LET HER LOOKS FOOL YOU, FOLKS--SHE'S ALL BUSINESS OUT THERE!
FRANK STROM • writer
DAVID ALVAREZ • penciller
MIKE DeCARLO • inker
JOHN COSTANZA • letterer
DAVE TANGUAY • colorist
HARVEY RICHARDS • assist
HEIDI MacDONALD • editor

NOW THAT'S WHAT I CALL A FINE SET OF WHEELS! RAWRR!
MEBBE SHE'LL LET ME ROTATE HER TIRES...!
ONE SIDE, ONE SIDE! RABBIT COMIN' T'ROUGH!
WHAT'S THIS? A ROGUE SKATER HAS HIT THE TRACK! LOOKS LIKE HE'S GOT HIS EYE ON QUEENIE.
OOPS! I STAND CORRECTED-- HE GOT EYES FOR QUEENIE!
AH, SUCH A REFINED VISION OF LOVELINESS! WHAT SAY YOU AN' ME MAKE TRACKS? HMM?
GIGGLE!
I THINK WE COULD HAVE A GREAT FUTURE IN PAIRS SKATING? WHADDAYA--
THUD
OOF!
EH, WHAT'S UP, DOC?
GRR! I...AM... THUD!
THERE MUST BE SOME MISTAKE. AIN'T THAT A SOUND EFFECT?

THUD!
OOOO, I HATE IT WHEN I'M RIGHT!!

SAYYY... YOUSE IS RIGHT! IT IS--IT IS A SOUND EFFECT!
I'D SAY I TOLD YOU SO, BUT I DON'T THINK MY MEDICAL PLAN WOULD COVER IT...!

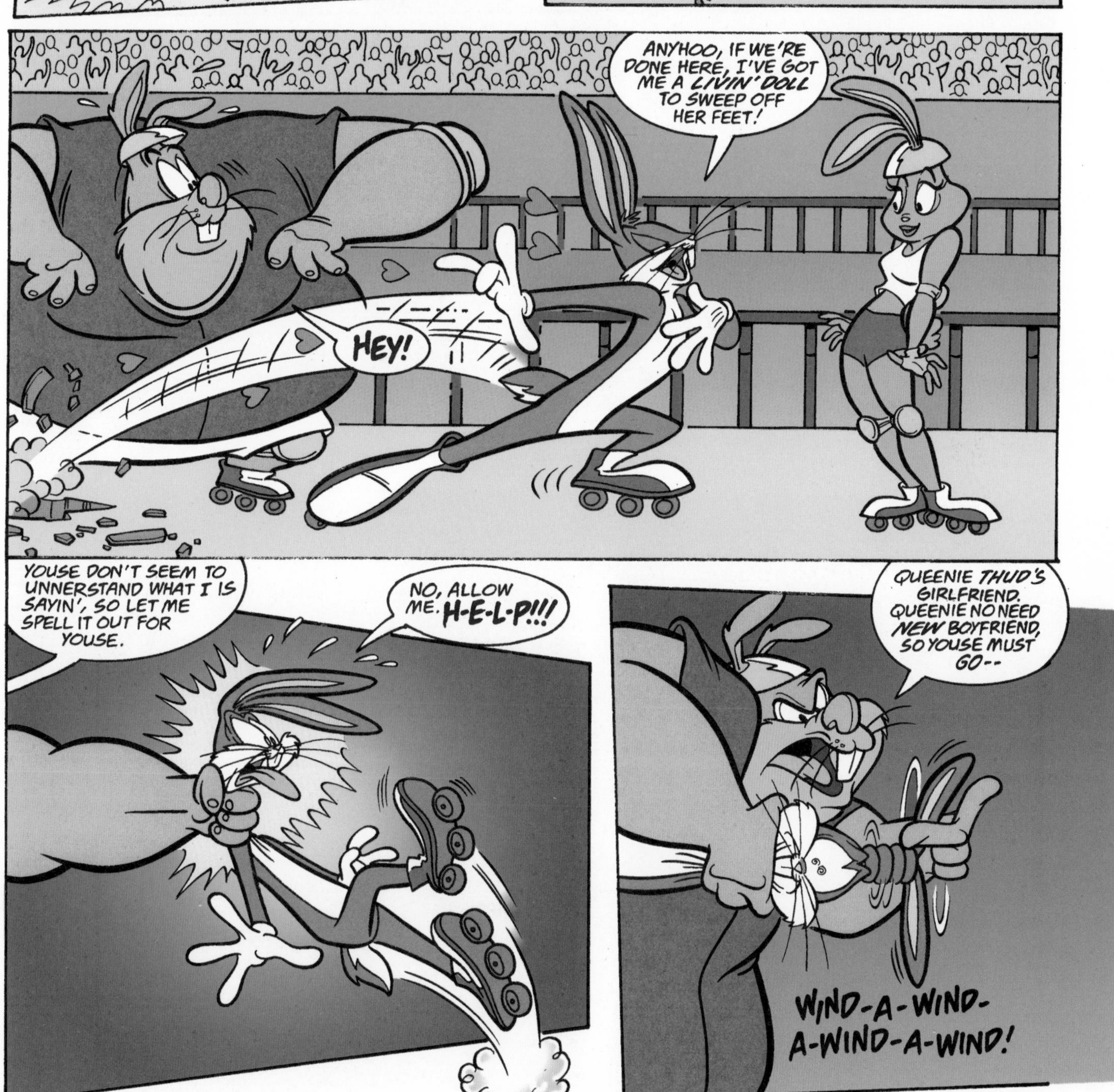
ANYHOO, IF WE'RE DONE HERE, I'VE GOT ME A LIVIN' DOLL TO SWEEP OFF HER FEET!
HEY!
YOUSE DON'T SEEM TO UNNERSTAND WHAT I IS SAYIN', SO LET ME SPELL IT OUT FOR YOUSE.
NO, ALLOW ME. H-E-L-P!!!
QUEENIE THUD'S GIRLFRIEND. QUEENIE NO NEED NEW BOYFRIEND, SO YOUSE MUST GO--
WIND-A-WIND-A-WIND-A-WIND!

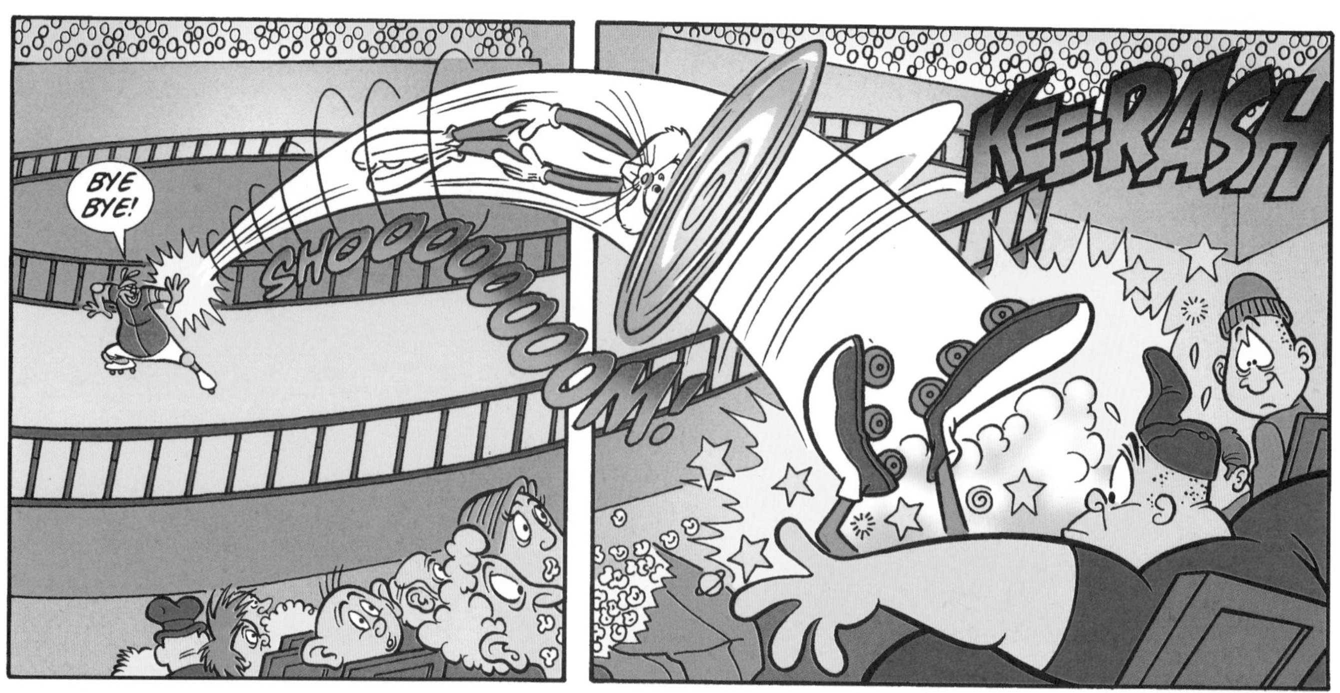

BYE BYE!
SHOOOOOOOOOOM!
KEE-RASH

GROAN!
YOU REALIZE, OF COURSE, THIS MEANS WAR...!

HERE'S DA DRILL... ONE BODY-CHECK OVER THE GUARDRAIL, FOR THIS CLOWN COMIN' UP!
ZOOOOOOOM!

THOMP!!

CHECK, PLEASE...

OKAY, I GOT IT WRONG THE FIRST TIME. WHEN DEALING WITH BIG GALOOTS ON ROLLER SKATES, IT'S BEST TO SPEAK SOFTLY AND CARRY A BIIIIG STICK!

ACK!
FERSHOOOOM!

OR WAS THAT "SPEAK BIGGLY AND CARRY A SOFT STICK"...?

WALLA WALLA
ALTOONA
5837
5
GOING INTO OUR SIXTH AND FINAL PERIOD, THE WIPEOUTS HAVE A COMMANDING 5832-POINT LEAD, WITH THREE MINUTES LEFT ON THE CLOCK!

IT'S NOW OR NEVER FOR THE ARM-BREAKERS! WILL THEY PULL VICTORY FROM THE JAWS OF DEFEAT, OR JUST LIE DOWN AND DIE LIKE THE WIMPS THEY ARE?

AND WHAT OF THIS MYSTERIOUS ROGUE SKATER? HOW WILL HE AFFECT THE OUT-COME OF THIS ALL-IMPORTANT MATCH-UP? WILL HE COST THE HOMETOWN HEROES THE WIN--

--OR WILL HE BE OVERCOME WITH THE SPIRIT OF SPORTS-MANSHIP AND FAIR PLAY?
ALL'S FAIR IN LOVE AN' WAR, BRUDDAH!
OILY KIDSTUFF

HE DOESN'T KNOW IT, BUT THUD'S ABOUT TO JOIN THE WIPEOUTS...!

AUGHH!!
SLIP!!

HEEHEEHEE! WHAT A MAROON! WHAT A SIMPLE-TOON! WHAT A DUMB BUNNY! WHAT A...

THUD!
SOMET'ING IS SORELY AMISS WITH THIS JOKE!
THUD SHOW QUEENIE WHO'S KING OF THE RINK!
BOY HOWDY! WHAT AN EXCITING TURN-AROUND THIS HAS BEEN! I'VE NEVER SEEN ANYTHING LIKE IT IN ALL MY YEARS AS A BROADCASTER...
ROLLER DERBY
...WITH ONLY 45 SECONDS OF GAME TIME LEFT, THUD HAS BRIDGED THE POINT GAP, LAPPING THE TRACK OVER 5000 TIMES!
IF HE CAN KEEP IT UP, HE'S A LOCK FOR THIS YEAR'S MVP AWARD!
HEE HEE! THUD MUST PRACTICE ACCEPTANCE SPEECH...!

UH-OH! I SPOKE TOO SOON! THE WIPEOUTS ARE CATCHING UP TO HIM...
WHAT? WHERE? WHO?

YEP! POOR THUD DOESN'T HAVE A PRAYER AGAINST THIS SORT OF ONSLAUGHT! THE WIPEOUTS ARE USING EVERY WEAPON IN THEIR ARSENAL--
W-W-WEAPON?

--BASEBALL BATS, NUNCHUKS, BILLY CLUBS, TENNIS RACKETS, FRYING PANS, ASSAULT TANKS, LASER CANNONS, SURFACE-TO-AIR MISSILES...
WHIMPER!

YESSIR, NOT EVEN THUD CAN POSSIBLY SURVIVE THIS BLOCKING MANEUVER!
BUT WAIT! THUD'S MAKING HIS BIG MOVE!
AAIIIIEEE!!!
FAHSHOOM

OOH, THAT'S GOTTA HURT! WELL, IT WASN'T PRETTY...
THUD!

...BUT THAT'S WHAT I CALL THE SHOW STOPPER! HEE HEE!
THAT'S ALL FOLKS!

A STRANGE OCCURRENCE IN A SMALL TOWN. AN UNIDENTIFIED FLYING OBJECT CRASHES. EVIDENCE OF AN ALIEN LIFEFORM? NOTHING BUT TRACKS LEADING TO A DINER. YOU'VE HEARD OF TRYING TO FIND A NEEDLE IN A HAYSTACK. TRY FINDING A MARTIAN IN A DINER... WHILE GRABBING A BITE IN *THE LOONEY ZONE*.
Looney Hound
WB1345

THIS IS THE LAST TIME I SUFFER THE INDIGNITY OF A PACKAGE TOUR! I THOUGHT WE'D NEVER STOP FOR SUSTENANCE.
WHAT'LL YA HAVE, DOLL?
A B.L.T., HOLD THE MAYO.
COMIN' RIGHT UP, MISTER.

THOSE FOOTPRINTS LEAD FROM THE SPACESHIP RIGHT TO HERE.

OK, PEOPLE... LISTEN UP! WE'VE GOT A SMASHED SPACESHIP OUTSIDE AND REASON TO BELIEVE THAT ONE OF YOU IS A CREATURE FROM ANOTHER PLANET!
SURRENDER, ALIEN, WHOEVER YOU ARE!
WHAT?!
GASP!

THAT FROZEN LACTOSE BEVERAGE WAS DELIGHT-FUL. I WOULD LIKE ANOTHER!

GOLLY! I WONDER WHICH *ONE* OF US COULD BE A *CREATURE* FROM ANOTHER *PLANET*?
I DON'T KNOW, MISTER. BUT NOBODY'S LEAVING 'TIL WE FIGURE IT OUT!

LOOK, PEOPLE. WE'RE GONNA SIT HERE UNTIL THE EXTRATERRESTRIAL AMONG US 'FESSES UP.
HIM!
MARS... COME IN, MARS...

OH, GIVE ME A BREAK! HOW HARD IS IT TO SPOT THE MARTIAN IN THIS CROWD? HUH? I MEAN, THE SHIFTY EYES, THE STRANGE BEHAVIOR, THE BIZARRE SPEECH. IT'S AS OBVIOUS AS THE BEAK ON MY FACE.

HE'S GOT A POINT, SARGE.
YEAH. I GUESS IT IS PRETTY CLEAR. GRAB 'IM.

I'M A DUCK, I TELL YA! JUST A REGULAR, RUN-OF-THE-MILL DUCK!

TELL IT TO THE SCIENTISTS, SPACE FREAK.
YEAH, WHILE THEY'RE PROBING YOUR BRAIN!

EXCUSE ME, KIND EARTHLING. DO YOU KNOW IF ANY OF YOUR SPECIES CAN REPAIR ASTRO LX33 SPACE MODULES?
NOPE. MORE COFFEE?
END

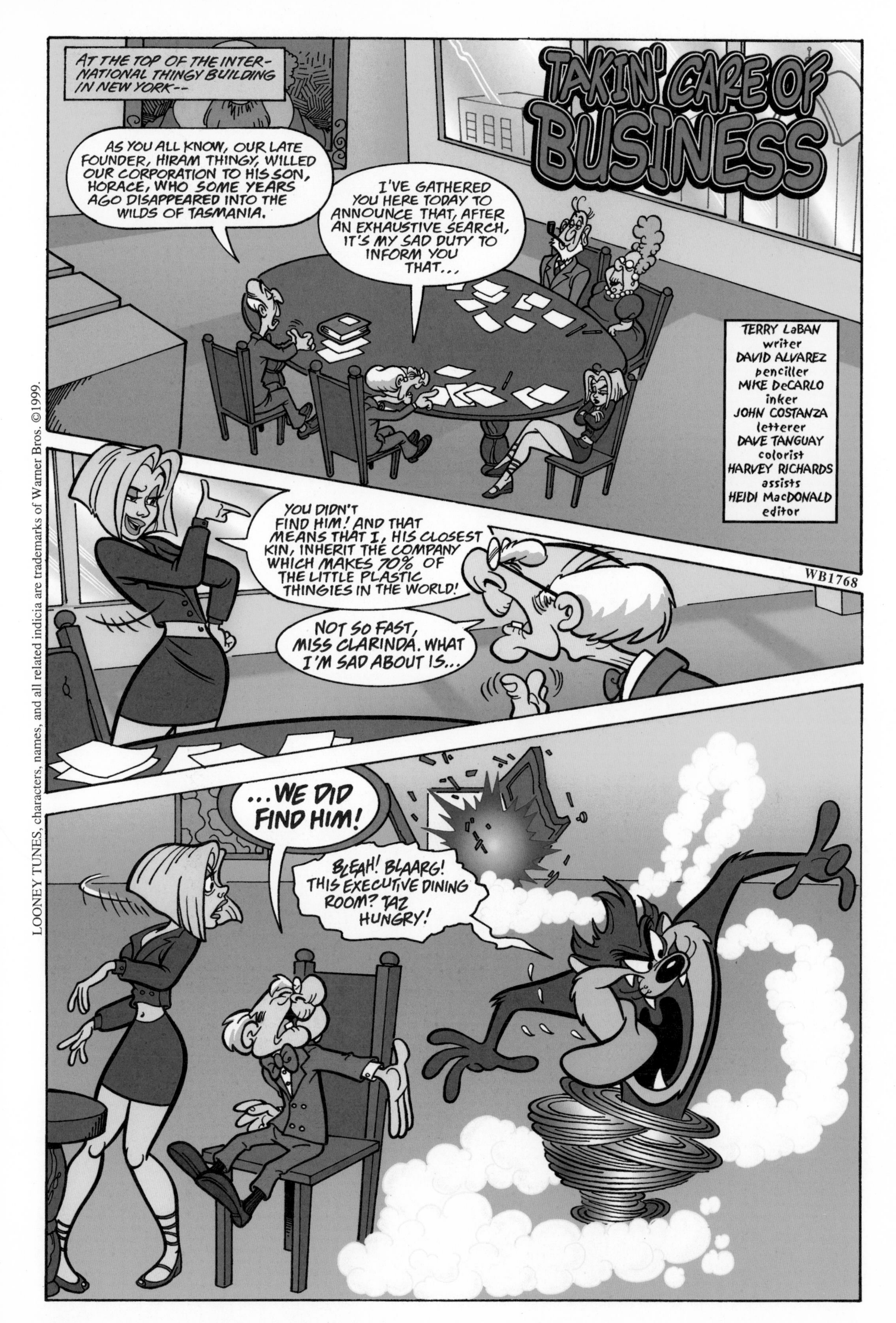

AT THE TOP OF THE INTERNATIONAL THINGY BUILDING IN NEW YORK--
TAKIN' CARE OF BUSINESS
AS YOU ALL KNOW, OUR LATE FOUNDER, HIRAM THINGY, WILLED OUR CORPORATION TO HIS SON, HORACE, WHO SOME YEARS AGO DISAPPEARED INTO THE WILDS OF TASMANIA.
I'VE GATHERED YOU HERE TODAY TO ANNOUNCE THAT, AFTER AN EXHAUSTIVE SEARCH, IT'S MY SAD DUTY TO INFORM YOU THAT...
TERRY LaBAN writer
DAVID ALVAREZ penciller
MIKE DeCARLO inker
JOHN COSTANZA letterer
DAVE TANGUAY colorist
HARVEY RICHARDS assists
HEIDI MacDONALD editor
YOU DIDN'T FIND HIM! AND THAT MEANS THAT I, HIS CLOSEST KIN, INHERIT THE COMPANY WHICH MAKES 70% OF THE LITTLE PLASTIC THINGIES IN THE WORLD!
WB1768
NOT SO FAST, MISS CLARINDA. WHAT I'M SAD ABOUT IS...
...WE DID FIND HIM!
BLEAH! BLAARG! THIS EXECUTIVE DINING ROOM? TAZ HUNGRY!

THAT'S HORACE? IT COULD BE ANY-ONE UNDER ALL THAT HAIR!
UNG! TASTE LIKE PAINT!
HORACE ALWAYS WAS A BIT UNTIDY. AND HE HAD A *TASTE* FOR ART.

BRAAAP! OILY FOOD GIVE TAZ GAS!
WELL, I SAY HE'S AN *IMPOSTOR!* IF YOU'RE *REALLY* HORACE, WHAT SECRET DID YOU TELL ME THE DAY BEFORE YOU LEFT FOR TASMANIA?

BLAH! GOORG! HUMMAGGG!
SMACK!
SO! IT *IS* YOU! I HATED THAT THE FIRST TIME YOU DID THAT AND I HATE IT EVEN *MORE* NOW!

TRY AGAIN? MAYBE IMPROVE TAZ'S TECHNIQUE!
MARK MY WORDS! INTERNATIONAL THINGY MAY BE YOURS FOR NOW-- BUT I'LL GET IT YET!
AND SO--
GOOD MORNING, SIR! HOPE YOU HAD A PLEASANT NIGHT. HERE'S YOUR CAR!
UNG! SMACK! TAZ LOVE TASTE OF FINE LIMOUSINE!
ER, MAYBE WE SHOULD CALL A CAB, SIR. THE STOCKHOLDERS ARE WAITING FOR YOU!

SOON--
YOUNG MAN, YOU HAVE A BIG JOB AHEAD OF YOU!
SINCE YOUR FATHER'S DEMISE, THE VALUE OF OUR SHARES HAS DROPPED BY HALF!
SHARE?
TAZ HATE TO SHARE!
WANT EVERYTHING FOR HIMSELF! MMMF! BRAGH!
HOLY COW!
THIS GUY TAKES NO PRISON-ERS!
THIS CALLS FOR IMMEDIATE ACTION!
SIDNEY! THE NEW CEO IS GONNA EAT THE COMPETITION ALIVE! BUY ME A HUNDRED MORE SHARES OF INTERNATIONAL THINGY!
THWIP!
THWIP!
TWO HUNDRED MORE SHARES!
THWIP!
THREE HUNDRED!
MUNNH! UMMF! YOU GUYS GOT KETCHUP?
IN A MATTER OF WEEKS--
FORPES
Thingy's New WILD MAN
BUSINESS TWEAK
Thingy Heir Kicks Business Booty
Wall Street Joinal
Thingy King-Y

SIR, THE QUARTERLY REPORTS ARE IN! WE'VE MADE RECORD PROFITS!
MMF! MWOOWF! TAZ NO LIKE RECAHDS! LIKE CDS!
ALL RIGHT, MY HAIRY COUSIN! THE PARTY'S OVER!
GASP! CLARINDA!
MY PARTNER, THE CEO OF GLOBAL DOODAD, AND I HAVE ACQUIRED ALMOST ALL YOUR STOCK! WE'RE BUYING INTERNATIONAL THINGY IN A HOSTILE TAKEOVER!
HOSTILE? TAZ SHOW YOU HOSTILE!
ARE YOU SURE? WOULDN'T YOU RATHER SPEND SOME TIME WITH THIS FINE NEW CAR?
CAAAAAH? TAZ LOOOVE GOOD CAAAH!
CLANG!
MMMF! RRNG! UH OH...

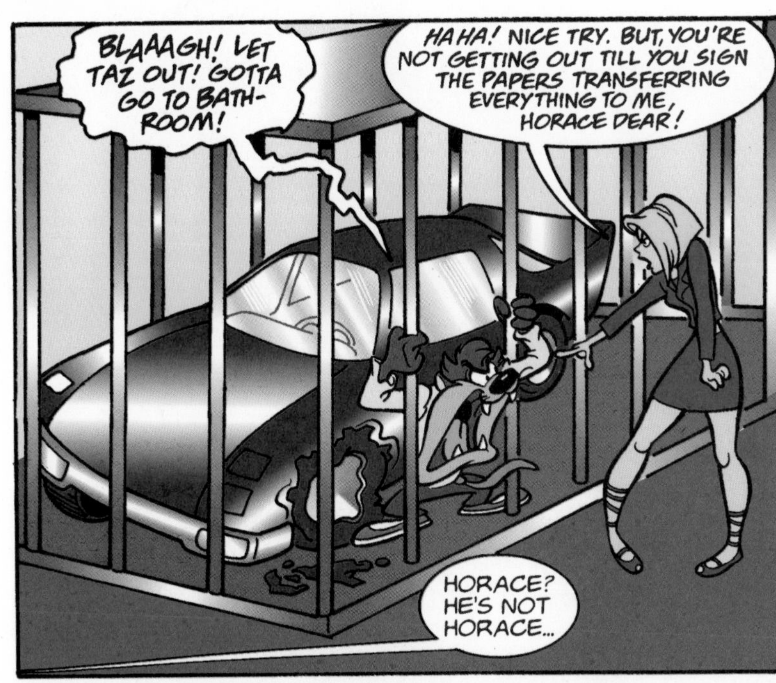
BLAAAGH! LET TAZ OUT! GOTTA GO TO BATH-ROOM!
HA HA! NICE TRY. BUT, YOU'RE NOT GETTING OUT TILL YOU SIGN THE PAPERS TRANSFERRING EVERYTHING TO ME, HORACE DEAR!
HORACE? HE'S NOT HORACE...

I AM!
Gasp! IT CAN'T BE!
OK! TAZ SIGN PAPERS!

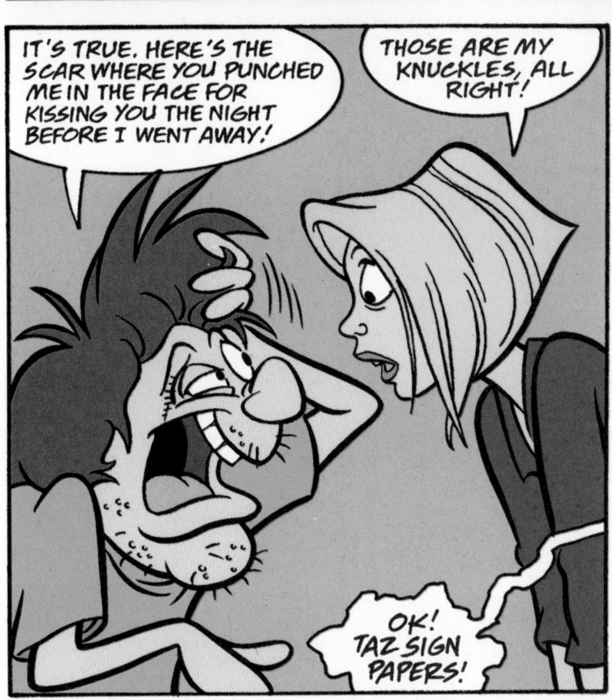
IT'S TRUE. HERE'S THE SCAR WHERE YOU PUNCHED ME IN THE FACE FOR KISSING YOU THE NIGHT BEFORE I WENT AWAY!
THOSE ARE MY KNUCKLES, ALL RIGHT!
OK! TAZ SIGN PAPERS!

BUT THEN... WHO'S THAT?
THAT? THAT'S A WILD, VICIOUS, TASMANIAN...
OK, AWREADY! TAZ SIGN PAPERS!

SMASH!

...DEVIL!
TO HECK WITH PAPERS! TAZ GOTTA GO!

WELL, IF YOU STILL WANT YOUR CORPORATION BACK, YOU OUGHT TO KNOW THAT I'M ABOUT TO TAKE IT OVER!
BLEEAH! YOU CAN HAVE IT. WHO WANTS TO WEAR A TIE EVERY DAY?

PHEW! TAZ FEEL BETTAH!
NOT FOR LONG, UGLY! YOU'RE FIRED!

BWAAAG! WAAAAH! TAZ DOWNSIZED! HOW HE GET ANUTHUH JOB AT HIS AGE?
DON'T WORRY, MY FRIEND! WE'D BE THRILLED TO HAVE SOMEONE OF YOUR ABILITY AT GLOBAL DOODAD!
BWAG! FUHGIT IT! TAZ TIRED OF CORPORATE POLITICS! HAVE BETTER IDEA!

SORRY! MAPLE GIVE TAZ GAS!
FOR THIS WE PAID 300 DOLLARS?
$TODAY'S SEMINAR$
GETTING RICH
THE TAZ WAY
THAT'S ALL FOLKS!

An Air to Remember

STARRING PEPE LE PEW -and- Penelope

I WEEL NEVER FORGET ZEES TIME WE HAVE SHARED, CHERIE...

MMMMNPH!! MMMPH!
...HOW LONG HAS EET BEEN? TEN, FIFTEEN MINUTES?

AAAAALLLL ASHORE!
QUEL DOMAGE!
AND SO ENDS OUR SENTI-MENTAL JOURNEY!
ALL RIGHT, YOU TWO--LET'S GO!
SPCA
SPCA

BEFORE WE PART, CHERIE, PROMISE ME ZEES... ZAT WE SHALL RENDEZVOUS A YEAR FROM NOW!
MEET ME AT ZE EMPIRE STATE BUILDING, YES?
SPCA

AH, SHE EEZ INARTICULATE WITH JOY! A YEAR FROM NOW EET EEZ!
A BIENTOT, MON PETIT CABBAGE! I SHALL WAIT FOR YOU IN ZE POKEY!
GASP! WHEEZE!

Writers: S.Carolan & J.Moore Pencils: D.Alvarez Inks: M. DeCarlo Letters: J.Costanza Colors: D.Tanguay Edits: D.Kurtin

364 DAYS LATER...
AT LONG LAST, I HAVE COME TO MEET MY LOVE!
OH, ZE ANTICIPATION! ZE ELATION! ZE EXCLAMATION!
EMPIRE STATE BUILDING
OBSERVATION DECK
LET ZE WOOING COMMENCE!!

AT THAT MOMENT...
TODAY IS ZE DAY, CHERIE! MEET ME AT ZE OBSERVATION DECK!
XXOO Pepe

ACME SHANGHAI DELIVERY SERVICE
ACME SHANGHAI DELIVERY SERVICE
WHOOSH!
BANGKOK

WHOOOOOSH
ZOOOM

Paddle
Paddle
Paddle

WHEW!

RRUMMMMBLE
RRRUMMMMBLE!!

FOOM!!

LE FEMMES, ALWAYS MAKING ZE BOYFRIEND WAIT...

SPLAT!!
DARLING!!

...SIGH!
OH DARLING, WE WEEL BE SO HAPPY TOGEZAIR... FOREVER!
THAT'S ALL FOLKS!

Writer: Brett Koth Pencils: Alvarez Inks: DeCarlo Letters: Costanza Colors: Tanguay Assists: Richards Edits: MacDonald

CITY SCRAPE

writer: MICHAEL EURY ·
pencils: NEAL STERNECKY ·
inks: MIKE DECARLO ·
letters: JOHN COSTANZA ·
color: DAVE TANGUAY

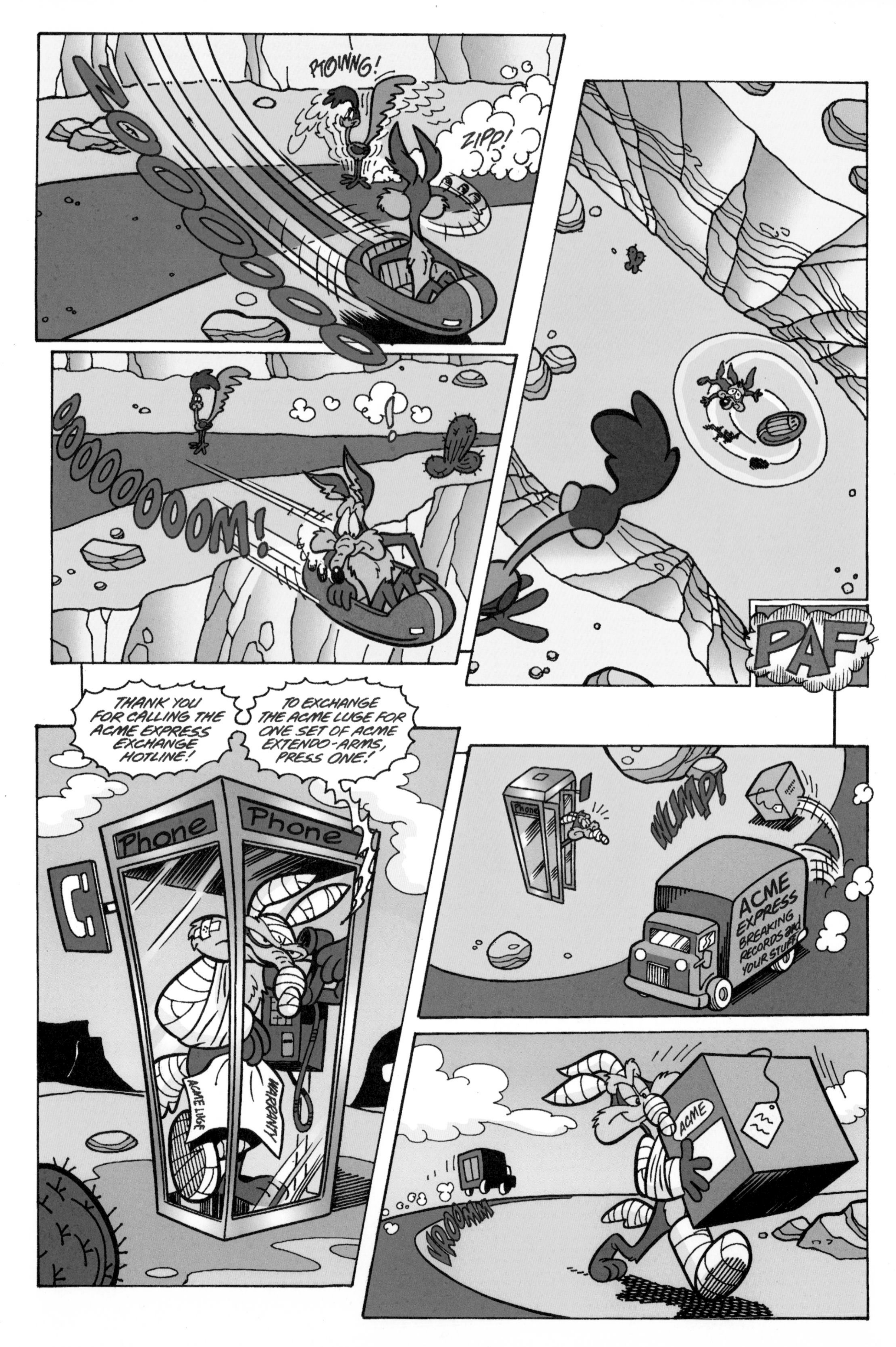
PTOIWNG!
ZIPP!
ZOOOOOOOOOOOOOOOOOOM!
!
PAF
THANK YOU FOR CALLING THE ACME EXPRESS EXCHANGE HOTLINE!
TO EXCHANGE THE ACME LUGE FOR ONE SET OF ACME EXTENDO-ARMS, PRESS ONE!
Phone
Phone
ACME LUGE
WARRANTY
WUMP!
ACME EXPRESS BREAKING RECORDS and YOUR STUFF!
ACME
VROOMM

BEEP BEEP!
SLURP!
ACME
PULL TAB TO OPEN
WHOOOM!
YANNK!
ACME
?!
FOOOM!
VOOP!
ZIPP

BEEP BEEP!
PULL!
CHARLIE
BEEP BEEP!
PAF
ACME CITY in a BOX
ATTENTION!

?
ACME CITY BOX
ATTENTION

The Acme Extending Arms are no longer in stock. As a replacement, here is Acme's CITY IN A BOX! Enjoy!
ACME CITY in a BOX

BEEP BEEP!

HONK HONK HONK HONK!
TOOT!
BEEP! BEE
HONK
BEEP BEEP!
BEEP
HONK
TAXI
SLOW

ZIPP!
HONK HONK
HONK
BEEP BEEP
TOOT!
TOOT

BEEP BEEP!
DING!
WHAMM!
DING!
DING!
WHAMM!!

PARK
5 LEVELS
NO WAITING!
HUFF! PUFF!
RK
5 LEVELS
NOWAITING
MEEP MEEP!

UNNNF
PUSH!

TO STREET

HAH!

?

!!
!

UMBRELLAS
$10.
ZIP!

LAS
ZIP!

WHAMM!

BEEP BEEP!

JUMP!

BEEP BEEP!
??!

SCHPLATT!
WHAM
BEEP BEEP!
HONK HONK
PUSH BUTTON TO DEFLATE ACME CITY IN A BOX
KTHUNK!

PFSHWUMP

ACME
CITY in a
BOX

ACME
CITY in a
BOX
SQUEEEEK
ACME
CITY in a
BOX

ACME
CITY in a
BOX

BOOT!
ACME
CITY in a
BOX
BOOT!

RRRUMMBLE

DESERT GETAWAY
CHARTER
!
PTUI!
BEEP
BEEP!

BEEP
BEEP!
HAVE A
HEART...
END THIS
HERE...
PLEASE!
OKAY!
THAT'S ALL
FOLKS!

Writer: Brett Koth Pencils: Alvarez Inks: DeCarlo Letters: Costanza Colors: Tanguay Assists: Richards Edits: MacDonald

YOU'VE GOT MAYHEM
words: TERRY LaBAN letters: JOHN COSTANZA
pencils: DAVID ALVAREZ colors: DAVE TANGUAY
inks: MIKE DeCARLO assists: HARVEY RICHARDS
edits: DANA KURTIN
OH DEAR! THESE NEWFANGLED GADGETS ARE SUCH A NUISANCE. THE MAN AT THE STORE TOLD ME I'D BE UP ONLINE IN A JIFFY, BUT THESE INSTRUCTIONS DON'T MAKE ANY SENSE! "ENTER NAME AT BLINKING CURSOR..."
IN MY DAY, WE'D GIVE A BLINKING CURSER A GOOD SPANKING, NEVER MIND TELLING HIM MY NAME!
LEMON COMPUTERS
PC
WB1680

I'M SURE THAT NICE YOUNG MAN AT THE STORE WON'T MIND HELPING ME. HE WAS SO GOOD ABOUT HELPING ME PICK OUT THE BEST, MOST EXPENSIVE COMPUTER!

I'LL BE GONE FOR JUST A BIT--
--MERCIFUL HEAVENS!

YOU STOP THAT RIGHT NOW, SYLVESTER!
WHEN I COME BACK, I EXPECT TO FIND MY COMPUTER JUST AS I LEFT IT--AND MY LITTLE TWEETY BIRD SAFE IN HIS CAGE!
THWAM

SLAM!
HEY! GET BACK IN YOUR CAGE! DIDN'T YOU HEAR WHAT GRANNY THSAID?!
NAW--I GOT WAX IN MY EARS.
HEY, LOOKIT ALL DEM LETTERS ON THE SCREEN!
PASSWORD VALID.
Please wait
for confirmation.

YOUR EARS'LL GO FIRST WHEN I GET HOLD OF YOU, Y'LITTLE PEST!
OOOH, CAREFUL, PUDDY! DIS THING AIN'T PAID FOR!
WHACK!

HA! GOTCHA, YOU MISTHER-ABLE...
GRAB!
WHAM!
TINKLE!
SPINK!
PING!

CONFIRMED
ACTUALLY... NOW I THINK I'M TH' ONE THAT 'TH MISTHERABLE...
AW, POOR PUDDY FALL DOWN GO CRASH-TINKLE-SPINK-PING?
HEY, WOOK AT DIS! SOMETHIN'S HAPPENIN' ON DA SCREEN!

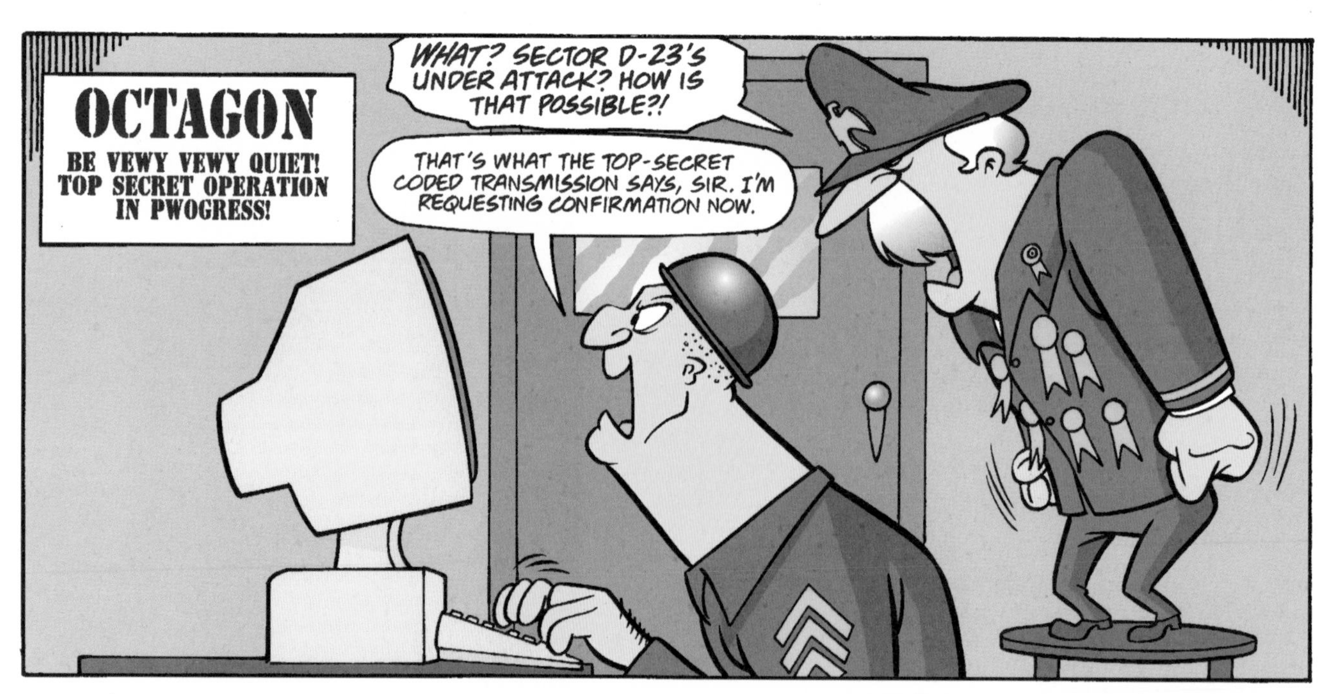
OCTAGON
BE VEWY VEWY QUIET! TOP SECRET OPERATION IN PWOGRESS!
WHAT? SECTOR D-23'S UNDER ATTACK? HOW IS THAT POSSIBLE?!
THAT'S WHAT THE TOP-SECRET CODED TRANSMISSION SAYS, SIR. I'M REQUESTING CONFIRMATION NOW.

Tiptoe on da keyboard wit' meeeee...
HEH HEH HEH...
CONFIRMED

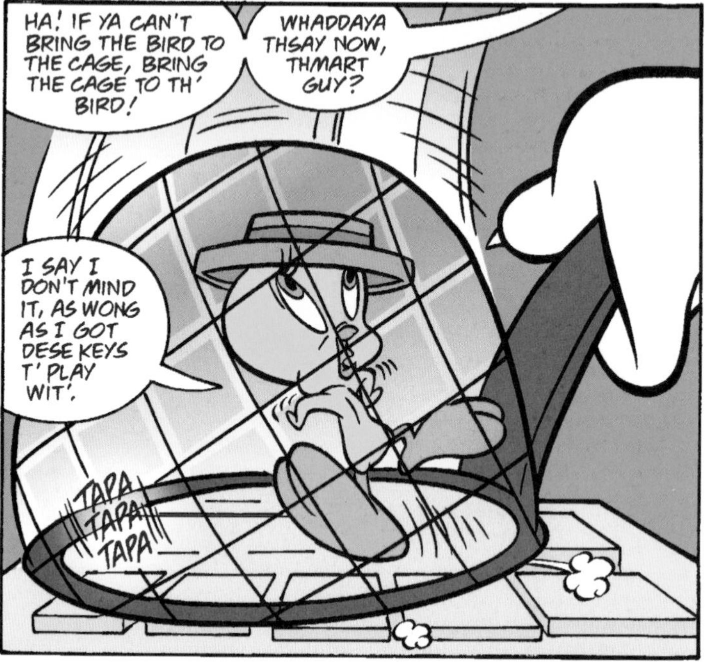
HA! IF YA CAN'T BRING THE BIRD TO THE CAGE, BRING THE CAGE TO TH' BIRD!
WHADDAYA THSAY NOW, THMART GUY?
I SAY I DON'T MIND IT, AS WONG AS I GOT DESE KEYS T' PLAY WIT'.
TAPA TAPA TAPA

DOGGONE IT, THSTOP HITTIN' TH' KEYSTH!
IN TH' CAGE, OUTTA TH' CAGE. MAKE UP YER MIND, PUDDY!
PONK!
CONFIRMED

THAT'S CORRECT, SIR! SECTOR D-23 IS UNDER ATTACK! THAT TRANSMISSION WAS IN OUR MOST TOP-SECRET ENCRYPTED CODE!
ALL FORCES ON HIGH ALERT! ASK THEM FOR THEIR COOR-DINATES!

THAT'STH IT! I'M GONNA DO WHAT I THSHOULD'VE DONE A LONG TIME AGO-- AND FRICASSTHEE YOU FOR GOOD!
WIDDLE ME? IT'S NOT WORTH IT, PUDDY TAT-- YOU'VE GOT PWENTY TO WIVE FOR!

AN' I'M GONNA HAVE A LOT MORE AFTER I-- WHOOPS!

SMASH!
OOPSIE! DAT PUDDY SURE IS CWUMSY!

OOOH, WHATTA MESS! GRANNY CAN'T WEAVE YOU AWONE FOR A MINUTE, CAN SHE?
I'M THSTARTING TO THINK IT'D BE A GOOD IDEA IF SHE NEVER DOESTH IT AGAIN...

UH OH-- I'VE LOST COMMUNICATION, SIR!
SO MUCH FOR THAT! WITHOUT THEIR COORDINATES, WE CAN'T POSSIBLY ATTACK! OH WELL, ANOTHER DAY, ANOTHER DOLLAR, EH?
OCTAGON
BE VEWY VEWY QUIET! TOP SECRET OPERATION IN PWOGRESS!

I APPRECIATE THIS SO MUCH, YOUNG MAN.
WHATEVER. IT'S YOUR DOUGH.
THE COMPUTER'S RIGHT THIS...
GASP! OH MY GRACIOUS! I WAS ONLY GONE TWENTY MINUTES AND SYLVESTER'S DESTROYED THE PLACE!
AND DON'T YOU DARE TRY TO BLAME IT ON MY DEAR LITTLE TWEETY, YOU BIG...
UH, LADY...
... IT DOESN'T TAKE BILL GATES T'FIGURE OUT THE COMPUTER WON'T WORK IF YA DON'T PLUG IT IN!

THEY'RE BACK! I HAVE THEIR COORDINATES, SIR!
YIPPEE! I MEAN, DARN! ALL FORCES PRO-CEED TO THE TARGET!

BUT I... I'M SURE IT WAS PLUGGED IN BEFORE!
SUUURE IT WAS! WHADDAYA NEED T'KNOW NEXT? HOW T'PUSH THE KEYS?

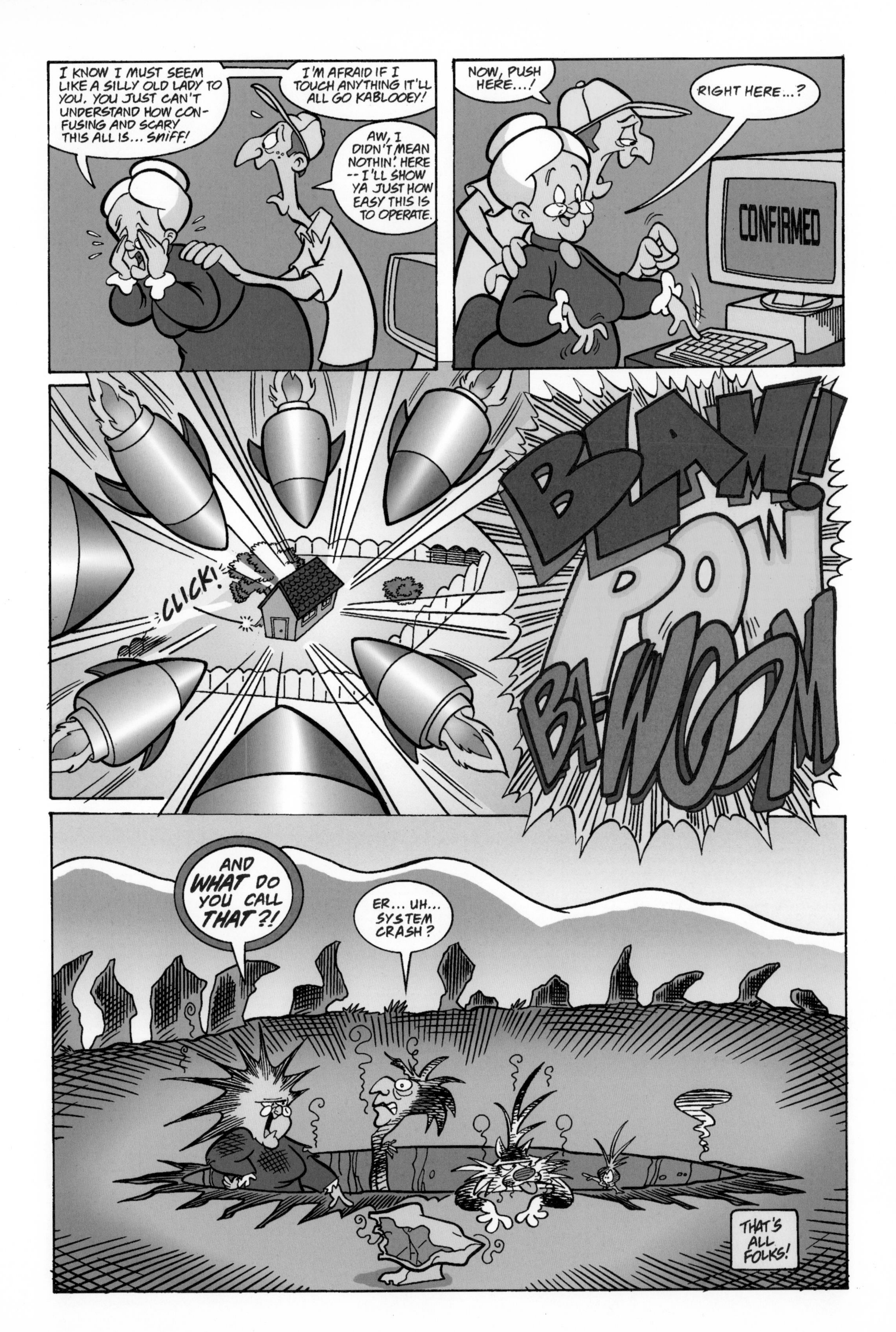
I KNOW I MUST SEEM LIKE A SILLY OLD LADY TO YOU. YOU JUST CAN'T UNDERSTAND HOW CONFUSING AND SCARY THIS ALL IS... SNIFF!
I'M AFRAID IF I TOUCH ANYTHING IT'LL ALL GO KABLOOEY!
AW, I DIDN'T MEAN NOTHIN'. HERE -- I'LL SHOW YA JUST HOW EASY THIS IS TO OPERATE.
NOW, PUSH HERE...!
RIGHT HERE...?
CONFIRMED
CLICK!
BLAM!
POW
BA-WOOM
AND WHAT DO YOU CALL THAT?!
ER... UH... SYSTEM CRASH?
THAT'S ALL FOLKS!

Writer: Brett Koth Pencils: Alvarez Inks: DeCarlo Letters: Costanza Colors: Tanguay Assists: Richards Edits: MacDonald

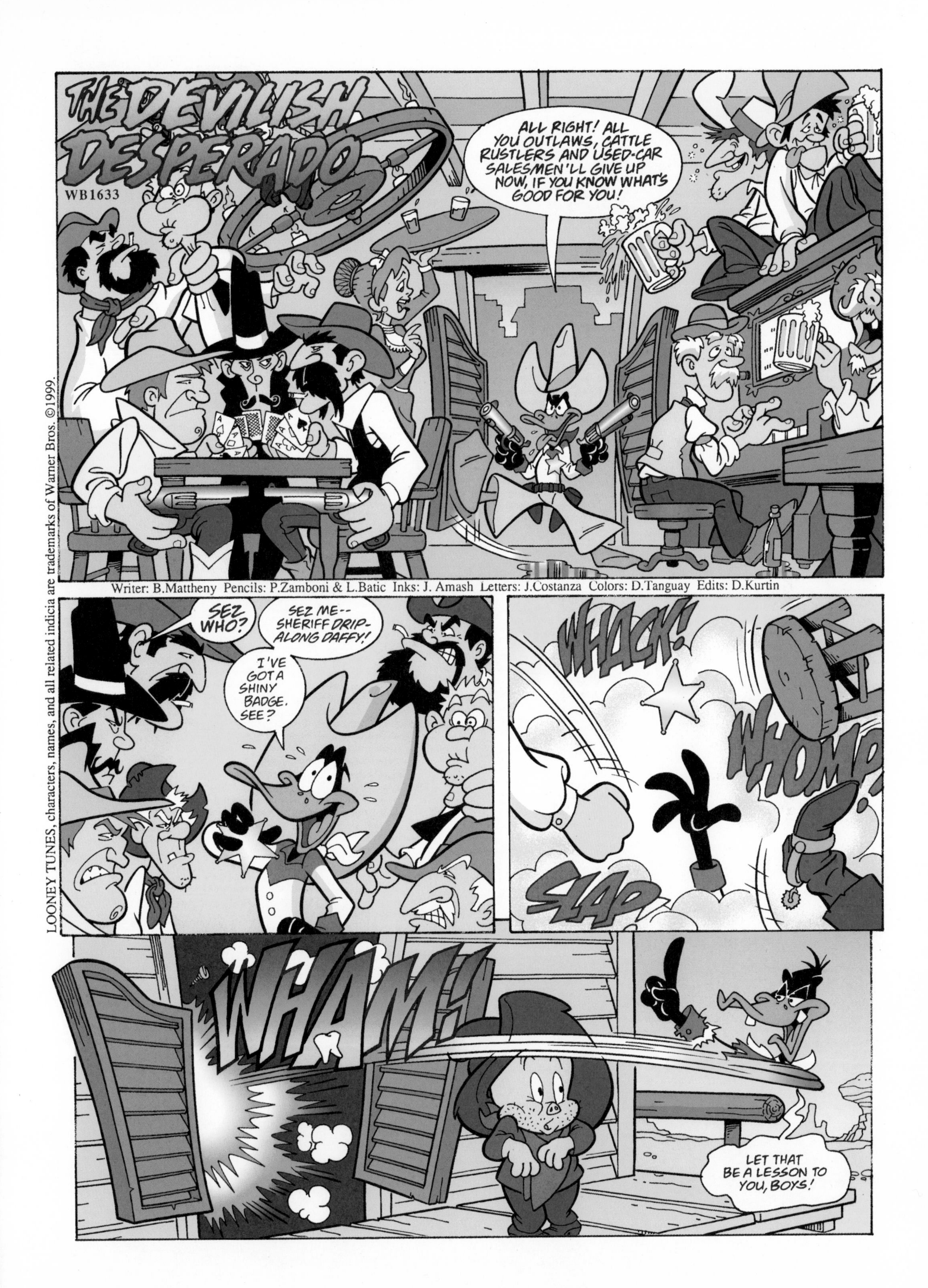
THE DEVILISH DESPERADO
WB1633
ALL RIGHT! ALL YOU OUTLAWS, CATTLE RUSTLERS AND USED-CAR SALESMEN'LL GIVE UP NOW, IF YOU KNOW WHAT'S GOOD FOR YOU!
Writer: B.Mattheny Pencils: P.Zamboni & L.Batic Inks: J. Amash Letters: J.Costanza Colors: D.Tanguay Edits: D.Kurtin
SEZ WHO?
SEZ ME-- SHERIFF DRIP-ALONG DAFFY!
I'VE GOT A SHINY BADGE. SEE?
WHACK!
WHOMP!
SLAP
WHAM!
LET THAT BE A LESSON TO YOU, BOYS!

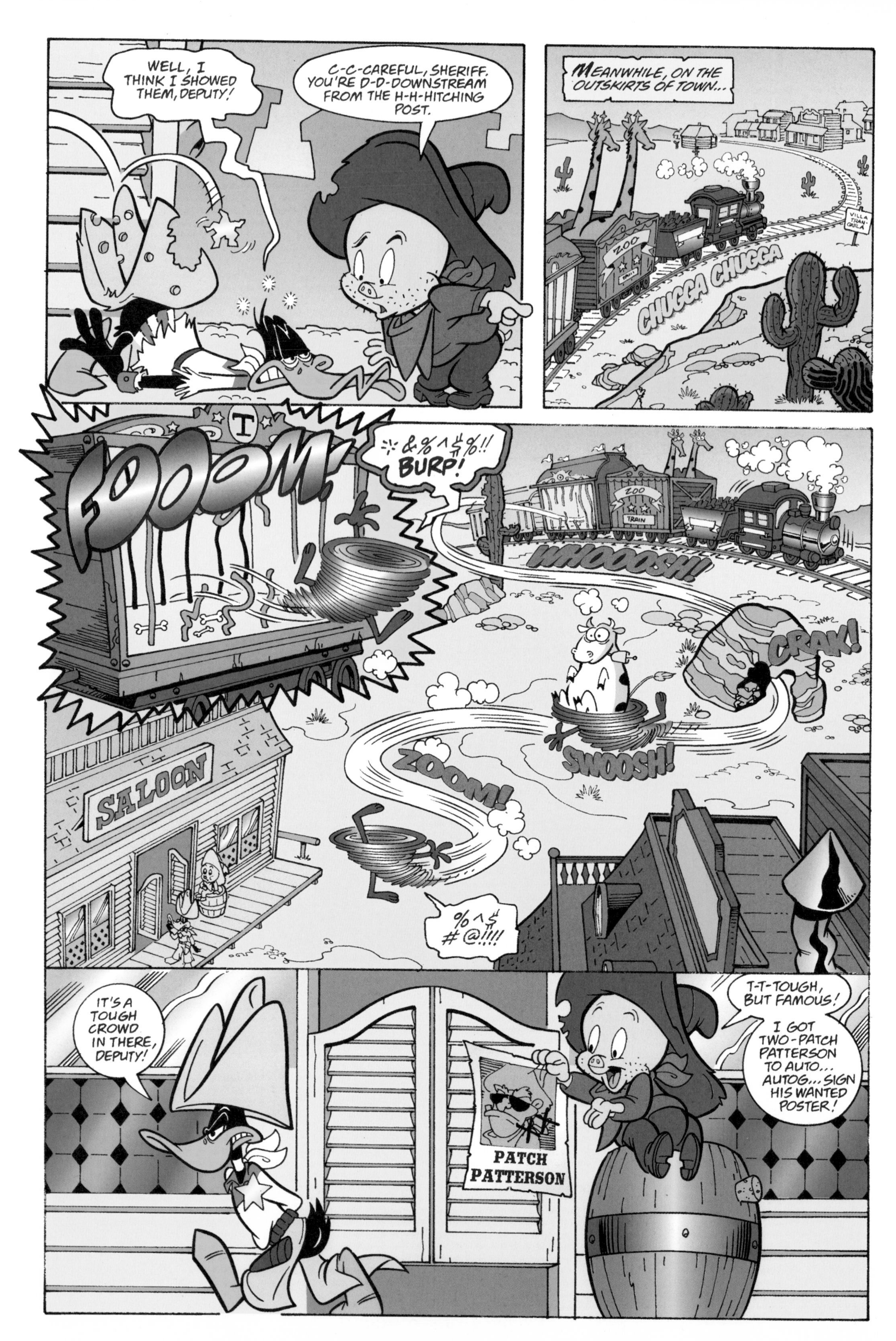
WELL, I THINK I SHOWED THEM, DEPUTY!
C-C-CAREFUL, SHERIFF. YOU'RE D-D-DOWNSTREAM FROM THE H-H-HITCHING POST.
MEANWHILE, ON THE OUTSKIRTS OF TOWN...
ZOO
CHUGGA CHUGGA
FOOOM!
&%^$%!! BURP!
ZOO TRAIN
WHOOOSH!
CRAK!
SALOON
ZOOM!
SWOOSH!
%^$ #@!!!!
IT'S A TOUGH CROWD IN THERE, DEPUTY!
T-T-TOUGH, BUT FAMOUS!
I GOT TWO-PATCH PATTERSON TO AUTO... AUTOG... SIGN HIS WANTED POSTER!
PATCH PATTERSON

IT WOULD TAKE A GENIUS TO STAND UP TO THOSE HOODLUMS-- ESPECIALLY THAT TWO-PATCH PATTERSON!
W-W-WHAT THE--

ZOUNDS! SOMEBODY'S TAKEN OUT TWO-PATCH PATTERSON!
CRASH! THUD! SMASH!
GOOD THING I ALREADY GOT HIS AUTO... AUTOG... SIGNATURE!
PATCH PATTERSON

ALL RIGHT, THAT'S ENOUGH, BUDDY!
IF THERE'S ANY RIFFRAFF TO BE ROUGHED UP, LET THE LAW HANDLE IT!
CRUNCH, CRUNCH MMMM?

^&%$#@!!
HEY!
R-R-RIP!

WHAT'S THE BIG IDEA?
I HAD TO EAT 20 BOXES OF CEREAL TO WIN THAT BADGE!
GULP!

HUH?
COUGH IT UP, BUSTER!
THAT'S GOVERNMENT PROPERTY YOU'RE SNACKING ON!

GULP!
SH-SH-SHERIFF!

YOU SPIT HIM OUT RIGHT NOW!
IT'S ILLEGAL TO GNAW ON A SHERIFF WITHOUT HIS AGREE... AGREEM... OKAY!

PTOOEY!

EGADS! HIS SALIVA HAS STAINED MY CHAPS! THAT DOES IT!
WATCH CLOSELY AND SEE HOW A TRAINED LAWMAN HANDLES THIS, DEPUTY!
OH, I WILL, SHERIFF! JUST LET ME KNOW WHEN HE ARRI... ARRI... GETS HERE!

REMEMBER, I AM A CHAMPION RODEO ROPER!

AND YOU WON THE WATERMELON SEED SPITTING TRI...TRIA...CONTEST, TOO!
THREE TIMES IN A ROW!

GOT HIM!
MOTHER!
ZZZIP!

STOP IN THE NAME OF THE LAW! NOT TO MENTION MY CHIROPRACTOR!
%&$#@!!
URGH!
WHOMP!

HEY, WHERE ARE YOU GOING, CHUBBY?
BUT, SH-SH-SHERIFF! THAT'S A TASMANIAN DEVIL! THEY'RE REALLY DANGER... DANGER... REALLY MEAN!

THEN WE'LL FIGHT FIRE WITH FIRE! STAND BACK DEPUTY, I'M TRANS-FORMING MYSELF INTO A--
--TAS-MANIAN DUCK!

%^$#@!!!
OH GOODN... GOODNE... DEAR!

&^^& %#!!!!
HUH?
TASMANIAN...
DUCK?
THAT'S **RIGHT, BUSTER!**

I MOVE LIKE YOU MOVE, THINK LIKE YOU THINK!
AND AFTER MISSING A FEW BATHS, I'LL SMELL LIKE YOU SMELL!
SHERIFF! YOUR MUSCLES ARE SO BI... BI... HUGE! WHEN DID THAT HAPPEN?
SAY, THAT'S A GOOD QUESTION. THEY NEVER WORKED BEFORE!
WHAM!

THAT DOES IT! I'M CHALLENGING YOU TO A SHOWDOWN! MANO A MANO! DUCK TO DEVIL!
GASP!

SINCE YOU DON'T HAVE A GUN, WE'LL PLAY HIDE AND SEEK! LOSER LEAVES TOWN.
OOH, OHHH! YEAH, YEAH, YEAH!

I'LL HIDE FIRST. YOU COVER YOUR EYES AND COUNT TO TEN.
REMEMBER, NO PEEKING!
OKAY! OKAY!

ONE... UH, ONE... UH...

SHERIFF! ISN'T THIS CHEA... CHEAT... NOT FAIR?
OF COURSE NOT! FIRST RULE OF SHERIFF-ING: ALL'S FAIR IN LOVE AND HIDE AND GO SEEK!
Heh, Heh!
UH... ONE! YEAH!
TNT
TNT
BOOOM!!
READY OR NOT, HERE TAZ COME!
MOM, THE NACHOS ARE TOO SPICY!

ANYONE... GOT... MILK...?
LOOK, BOY! A SN...SNA... BONE!

CHUGGA CHUGGA
ZOO
GET IT, BOY! GET THE BONE, BOY!
BONE! YUM! YUM!

YEAH! YEAH!
BONK

W-W-WAKE UP, SHERIFF! YOU DID IT!
YOU THR... THRASH... BEAT THE TASMAN... TASMANA... HIM!
I DID?

I MEAN, OF COURSE I DID!
I, UH, MUST'VE STEPPED OUT TO THE LITTLE SHERIFF'S ROOM WHILE IT HAPPENED!

AHEM!
LADIES AND GENTLEMEN OF GUTROT GULCH, THANKS TO ME, YOUR BELOVED SHERIFF, THE TOWN IS ONCE AGAIN SAFE AND SOUND!
NOW LET'S TALK REWARD!

WHAT DO YOU MEAN? THANKS TO YOU, WE DON'T HAVE A TOWN!
YEAH!

GET HIM!
COME BACK HERE!
BLAM
BLAM!
WAIT! STAY BACK! I'M MOLTING AND IT MIGHT BE CONTAGI- OUS!
LOOKS LIKE GUTROT GULCH MAY HAVE A JOB OPENING AT THE SHERIFF'S OFFICE.
ANY T-T-TAKERS?
That's all Folks!

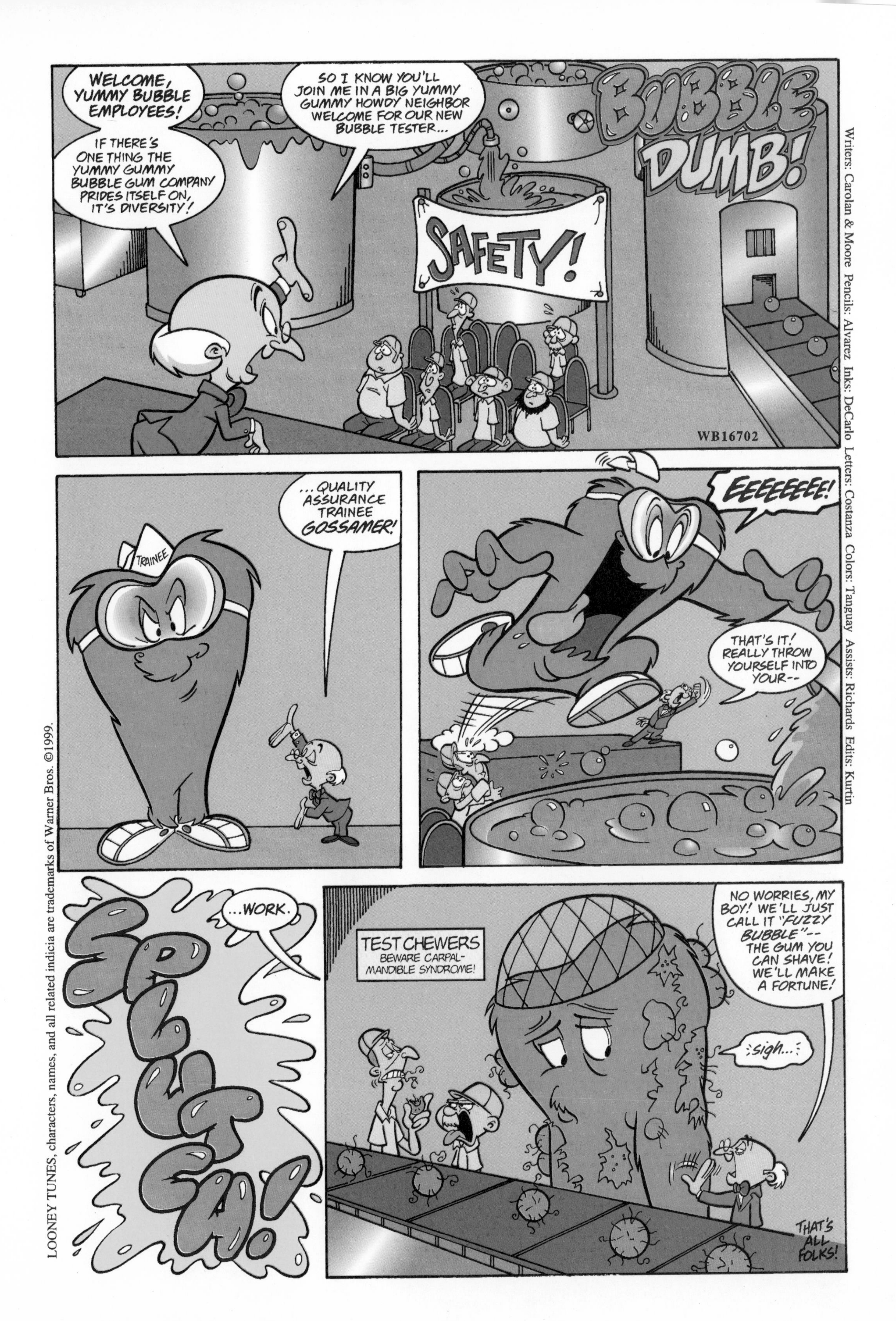
BUBBLE DUMB!
Writers: Carolan & Moore Pencils: Alvarez Inks: DeCarlo Letters: Costanza Colors: Tanguay Assists: Richards Edits: Kurtin
WELCOME, YUMMY BUBBLE EMPLOYEES!
IF THERE'S ONE THING THE YUMMY GUMMY BUBBLE GUM COMPANY PRIDES ITSELF ON, IT'S DIVERSITY!
SO I KNOW YOU'LL JOIN ME IN A BIG YUMMY GUMMY HOWDY NEIGHBOR WELCOME FOR OUR NEW BUBBLE TESTER...
SAFETY!
WB16702
...QUALITY ASSURANCE TRAINEE GOSSAMER!
TRAINEE
EEEEEEEE!
THAT'S IT! REALLY THROW YOURSELF INTO YOUR--
SPLUTCH!
...WORK.
TEST CHEWERS
BEWARE CARPAL-MANDIBLE SYNDROME!
NO WORRIES, MY BOY! WE'LL JUST CALL IT "FUZZY BUBBLE"-- THE GUM YOU CAN SHAVE! WE'LL MAKE A FORTUNE!
sigh...
THAT'S ALL FOLKS!

Written by: Michael Eury Art by: Nelson Luty and Horracio Ottolini
Lettered by: John Costanza Colored by: Jahrome Youngker

HOIMMMMM
SCREECH
RRRRR!
THAT'S THE LAST TIME I LET YOU DRIVE!
whimper

NOW THAT WE'VE ARRIVED, K-9, WE MUST COMMENCE WITH OUR MISSION--
--TO CONQUER THIS GARGANTUAN CITY, SHRINK IT TO MINUSCULE SIZE USING MY MARTIAN MINIATURIZER, AND ENTRAP IT PERMANENTLY WITHIN A SNOW DOME...
...AS I DID WITH ANOTHER COLOSSAL CURIOSITY, SUCH AS THE COLLAGEN-ENHANCED LIPS OF A FAMOUS HOLLYWOOD ACTRESS.
PREPARE FOR LANDING, TROOPS!
ATTENTION, EARTH CREATURES! I HEREBY CLAIM YOUR PATHETIC METROPOLIS IN THE NAME OF THE PLANET MARS!
THE DUCK DODGERS CONVENTION IS AT THE GARDEN, YA DIMWIT!!
OH, DARN. NO ONE SEEMS TO NOTICE ME. PERHAPS I SHOULD SPEAK LOUDER...
EARTHLINGS! YOUR CITY IS NOW MARTIAN PROPERTY!
HEY, HONEY, THIS MUST BE A PROMOTION FOR ONE OF THOSE FLYING SAUCER PICTURES.
RAP RAP
GOTTA BE A LOW-BUDGET MOVIE, THOUGH--LOOK AT THIS CHEESY COSTUME.
NOW SMILE, E.T. THIS ONE'S FOR THE FOLKS BACK HOME.
THIS IS THE MOST EXCITING THING THAT'S HAPPENED TO US SINCE WE SAW REGIS AT THAT DELI!

I MUST EMPLOY MORE DRAMATIC MEASURES TO CONVINCE THESE EARTHLINGS OF MY INTENTIONS.
SURRENDER NEW YORK TO ME, OR FACE YOUR OBLITERATION!
YO! SHORT STUFF!
C'MON, LI'L DUDE, COUGH UP YER WALLET.
BACK AWAY, HUMANOID! I WIELD A WEAPON OF UNFATH-OMABLE POWER-- THE ACME DISINTEGRATING PISTOL!
THAT'S WHAT 'CHU CALL IT. LOOKS LIKE FIFTY BUCKS FROM TH' CORNER PAWN SHOP TO ME.
OH, DEAR. THAT WASN'T A BIT NICE.
THANKS FOR TH' DONATION, MAN!
THIS IS A MOST UNEXPECTED DEVELOPMENT. UNEXPECTED, INDEED.
GUARD OUR SHIP, K-9, WHILE I CONVERGE UPON THIS "PAWN SHOP" TO RETRIEVE MY ACME DISINTE-GRATING PISTOL.
RUF!

DON'S PAWN & Hair Salon
THIS WEEK'S SPECIALS: VIDEO GAMES and BUZZCUTS
CA$H PAID FOR POPSICLE STICKS
WHAT A DISGRACEFUL ESTABLISHMENT. SIMPLY DISGRACEFUL.
PARDON ME, HOMO SAPIEN.
WHAT'D YOUSE CALL ME?
I SEEK A RECENTLY PAWNED WEAPON OF UN-FATHOMABLE DESTRUCTION.
'ZAT SO...?
CRANK DIS BABY ALLA WAY UP, AN' YOUSE'LL DESTROY EARDRUMS!!
♫ HEY, ♪ MACARENA!!
I DID NOT COME HERE TO LISTEN TO EARTH MUSIC, YOU LOWER LIFEFORM! ALTHOUGH I MUST ADMIT THAT TUNE GAVE ME THE PECULIAR URGE TO PERFORM A MINDLESS DANCE.
I WISH TO RE-ACQUIRE MY ACME DISINTEGRATING PISTOL! IT WAS BROUGHT TO YOU MOMENTS AGO BY A SCURRILOUS INDIVIDUAL.
YOUSE MEAN DIS? YEAH, SOME GUY JUS' BRUNG IT IN. PURTY COOL, AIN'T IT?
CAREFUL! YOU CAN'T IMAGINE THE DAMAGE THAT CAN CAU--

ZZZZZZARK!
OH, HEAVENS!
PACKS A PUNCH, DON'T IT?
AH... YES, IT DOES. NOW, HOW MUCH ARE YOU ASKING FOR IT?
HOW MUCH YOUSE GOT?
I HAVE TWO ILLUDIUM CRYSTALS, WORTH A FORTUNE ON MY WORLD...
... BUT VALUED AT APPROXIMATELY $ 2.39 ON EARTH.
NOT ENUFF, PALLY.
BUT I MUST OBTAIN MY ACME DISINTEGRATING PISTOL! I CAN'T ENSLAVE NEW YORK WITH-OUT IT!
TELL YOUSE WHAT, BUDDY...
... I'LL TAKE THEM CRYSTALS-- AND YOUSE SHOES. SNEAKERS IS A HOT ITEM 'ROUND HERE.
BUT I CAN'T TRAMPLE YOUR CITY IN BARE FEET!
'CAUSE I'M A NICE GUY, I'LL T'ROW IN A PAIR'A REPLACE-MENT SHOES, ABS'LUTELY FREE.
SHOES
OH, FOR JOY.

OH, MY. THE PRICE OF PLANETARY DOMINATION CAN SOMETIMES BE HIGH--
DON'S PAWN & Hair Salon
--LIKE THESE HEELS.
?
YOU'VE OBVIOUSLY NEVER SEEN A WORLD CONQUEROR BEFORE.
FRANK'S FURTERS
DEAR ME! THOSE EARTH CRETINS HAVE SULLIED MY SPACECRAFT!
NOW I SUPPOSE I'LL HAVE TO USE FORCE.
YOU THERE-- PREPARE TO BE DISINTEGRATED!
ZZZAARR!
RUN! HE'S PACKIN' HEAT!
ZZZZ RORISHK!

THIS IS NOT GOOD, NOT GOOD AT ALL.
AND I JUST HAD MY SHIP WAXED.
WHERE IS K-9?!! PROTECTING THE SPACECRAFT WAS HIS RESPONSIBILITY!
WE GOT CURBING LAWS IN NOO YAWK, FLEABAG!
ARFK! ARFK!
ARP ARP ARP ARP ARP ARP!
CITY POUND
THE AUTHORITIES HAVE APPREHENDED MY RESERVES!!
OH, DRAT.
STEADY, K-9! I'M--
PHLUP!
MEEP! MEEP! MEEP!
OH, PHOOEY! HOW WILL I EVER CATCH--?

A PRIMITIVE MODE OF TRANSPORTATION! HOW FORTUITOUS!
24 HOUR TAXI SERVICE LET US TAKE YOU FOR A RIDE 555-TAXI
FOLLOW THAT VEHICLE!
GO JAY-EFF-KAY?
EXCUSE ME...?
YON-KEE STAY-DYUM?
I'M HAVING DIFFICULTY COMPREHENDING YOU. ALLOW ME TO ANALYZE YOUR DIALECT WITH MY INTERGALACTIC LANGUAGE DESCRAMBLER.
HOW ODD...
DIALECT NOT LOCATED IN DATABASE OF 152,049 KNOWN LANGUAGES.
HOL-LEN TOE-NAIL?
CAN'T YOU GET IT THROUGH YOUR LOWER-ORDER BRAIN THAT I CANNOT UNDERSTAND YOU? AND WHY HAVE YOU STOPPED??!
I'VE ENDURED ENOUGH OF THIS!
WHERE'S MY FARE, YOU STINKIN' CHEAPSKATE?!
24 HOUR TAXI SERVICE

BARK
BARK
BARK!
CITY POUND
I'M HERE, K-9!
PREPARE TO BE LIBERATED!
ZZZZARK
CITY POUND
ZZZSHRANK!
OH, NO!
YIP! YIP! YIP!
BOW WOW
RUFF!

CHUNK!
OOH, THIS SILLY CITY IS SOOO IRRITATING!
GOODY GOODY. I BELIEVE I HAVE IT!
WHAT ELSE CAN GO WRONG WITH MY MISSION?
I HATE THIS CITY! I TRULY DO!
RELEASE MY FLYING SAUCER, AT ONCE!
STOP THAT TOW TRUCK!!

GREETINGS, NEIGHBOR. I'M THE MAYOR OF NEW YORK CITY...

...AND YOU'RE OUR 1,000,000TH TOURIST THIS YEAR! AS A TOKEN OF THE BIG APPLE'S GRATITUDE FOR VISITING US, I'M HAPPY TO PRESENT TO YOU--
--THE KEY TO THE CITY! TAKE MANHATTAN-- IT'S YOURS!
OOO, NO, THIS PLACE IS ABSOLUTELY DREAD-FUL!
I'D RATHER SPEND A YEAR ON PLUTO THAN ANOTHER MOMENT THERE.
SPUTTER
KLANNGG!
THE End

Writers: Sean Carolan & Jenn Moore Pencils: Alvarez Inks: DeCarlo Letters: Costanza Colors: Tanguay Assists: Richards Edits: Kurtin

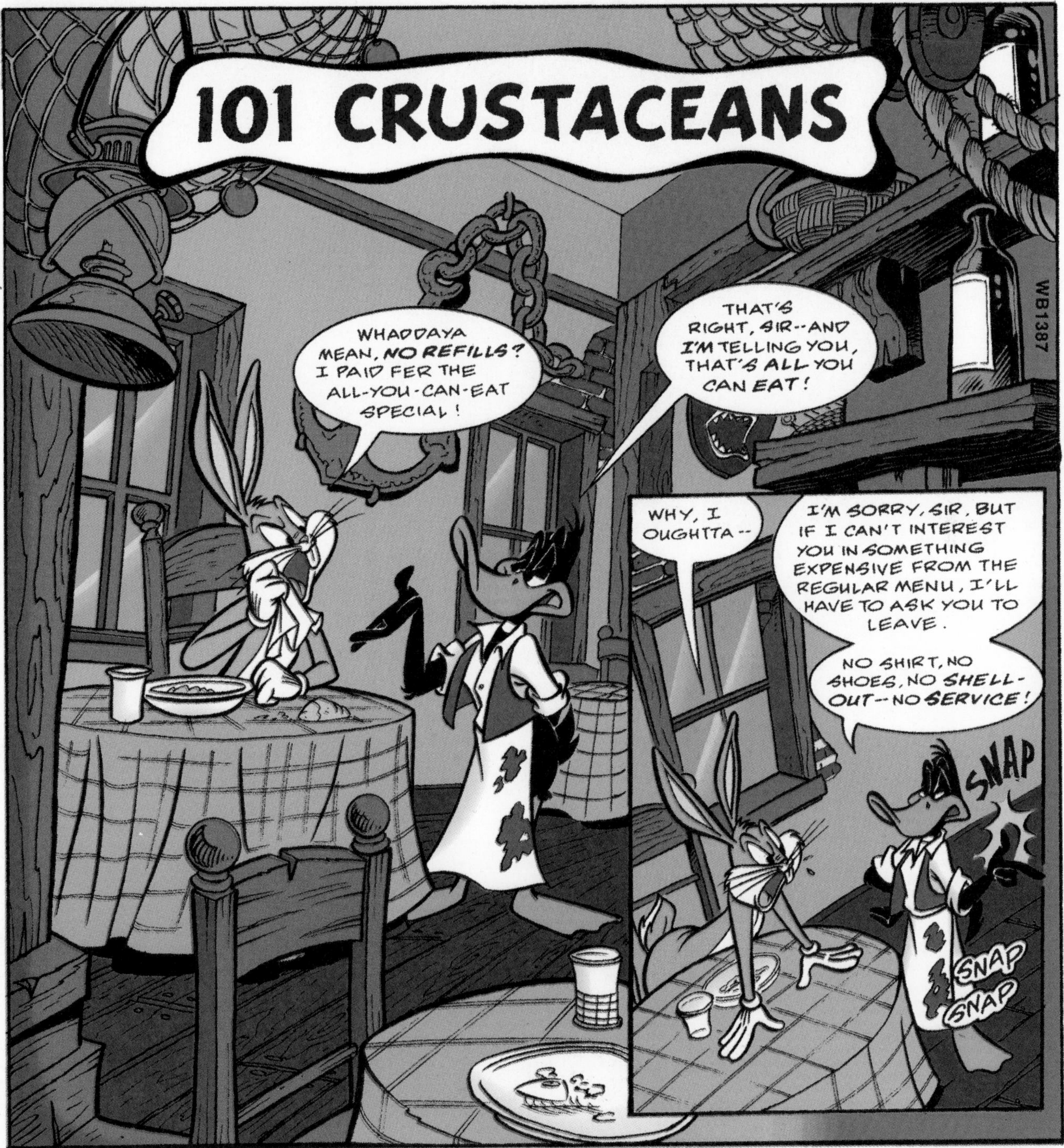

Writer:Terry Collins Penciller:Omar Aranda (Sol Studio) Inker:Horacio Ottolini(Sol Studio) Letterer:Lorina Mapa Colorist:Jahrome Youngker

DAAAH, YOU SNAPPED, BOSS?
HE SNAPPED A LONG TIME AGO, IF YOU ASK ME.

I HEARD THAT!
CRUSHER, KINDLY TAKE OUT OUR GUEST.
DAAAH, OKAY, BOSS!
POP
RIIIIP
SPANGG
GULP!

WE COULD GET SOMETHIN' TO EAT.
DAAAH, OKAY. BUT NOT HERE. I HEAR THE FOOD IS TERRIBLE.

I DIDN'T MEAN ON A DATE, YOU NINCOMPOOP!
SHOW HIM THE EXIT! BOOT HIM OUT THE DOOR! REMOVE HIM!
OH. OKAY. YOU GOT IT, BOSS.

DAAAH, ENJOY YOUR EVENING!
PUNT
YIPE!

WELL, THAT CRACKS IT. I'M DEFINITELY NOT RECOMMENDIN' DIS PLACE TO MY FRIENDS.

WEEEEELLLL... MMMMMAYBE ONE FRIEND...

HELLO, TAZ? IT'S ME, BUGS BUNNY. I WAS THINKIN' WE COULD GRAB A BITE --

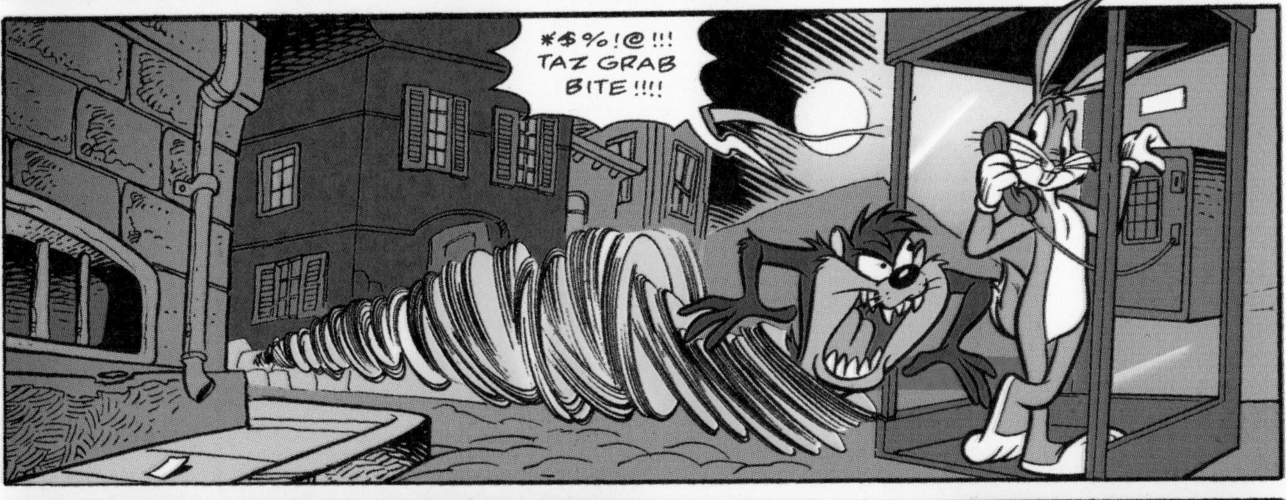
*$%!@!!! TAZ GRAB BITE!!!!

NAH NAH NAH, NOT ME, HERCULOID. SHEEZ, SOME PEOPLE! I THOUGHT WE'D GET SOME SEAFOOD!
%^$$@!! SEAFOOD?!! %^$#$@!

&*!! TAZ LIKE SEAFOOD!
SURE YA DO, DOC! JUST PUT ON THIS COAT AN' HAT...
OH, DARN, FORGOT SOME-THIN'! YOU GET STARTED WITHOUT ME, AND I'LL BE BACK IN A MO'!

%^&$#!!$ HUNGRY!!! TAZ WANT SEAFOOD! TAZ WANT LOBSTAAA!
WELCOME TO SEAFOOD GROTTO, WHERE IF YOU SEE FOOD, YOU EAT IT!
CAN I TAKE YOUR HAT, YOUR COAT, YOUR WALLET?
HEH-HEH!

SNIFF SNIFF
WHAT SMELL?
OH, ER, THAT'S PROBABLY TODAY'S SPECIAL OR IT COULD BE...

SNIFF SNIFF

NO, THAT'S DEFINITELY THE SPECIAL...
TAZ THINK HE PASS ON SPECIAL...

LOBSTAAA! %^#!! TAZ WANT LOBSTAAA!
EXCELLENT! PERHAPS AN APPETIZER BEFORE YOU START?
MENU

UMPH
ORF
SMAK
GOBBLE
ORP

URRRP!
NEEDS SALT.
MAY I OFFER YOU A SODA OR OTHER BEVERAGE TO WASH DOWN YOUR MENU?

TAZ WANT *#@!!!$ LOBSTAAA!
YES, WELL, WE'RE KNOWN FOR OUR AHEM "LOBSTAA", BUT IT'S RATHER EXPENSIVE.
LET'S SEE SOME CASH FIRST, BUB.

WHAT AM I THINKING?! YOU DON'T HAVE ANY MONEY! YOU'RE NOT EVEN WEARING PANTS!

WHERE *&^$$#!! LOBSTAAA?!
WOULD YOU BELIEVE WE'RE ALL OUT?

TAZ WANT LOBSTAAA NOW !!!
ANYONE EVER TELL YOU YOU'VE GOT A ONE-TRACK MIND ?

ANOTHER SATISFIED CUSTOMER, EH DOC ?
OW!
I'LL DEAL WITH YOU LATER, CARROT-BREATH !

THAT GOURMET GLUTTON IS TRASHING THIS JOINT !
ACTUALLY, I'D SAY THAT'S AN IMPROVEMENT.

WHERE %$^*!!!* LOBSTAAA ???
YOO HOO ! OH, CRUSHER-- COULD I SEE YOU FOR A MOMENT? LIKE NOW ?!

DAAAH, WHAT IS IT, BOSS ?
I'M RIGHT IN THE MIDDLE A' UNLOADING DESE LOBSTERS.

&%$#!!! LOBSTAAA YUM!!!
HEE HEE! STOP DAT!
DAT TICKLES!

ATTABOY, CRUSHER! GIVE HIM A LEFT! AND A RIGHT! AND A LEFT!

LOBSTAAAS! YEAH!!!
DAAH, COULD SOMEBODY UNTIE ME?
NO! NO!! NO!!!

YOU GOTTA HELP ME, BUGS! HE'S GONNA EAT ALL MY PROFITS!
EHHHH... I MIGHT HELP YOU OUT... FOR A FREE MEAL OR THREE.
ANYTHING! ANYTHING!

EASY THERE, DOC! YOU DON'T WANNA DO THAT.
YES TAZ %.&#@$!!! DO! WHY NOT?

HONK

...EHHHH...'CAUSE THEY AIN'T BEEN COOKED YET.
**&#$$!!! OW OW OW!!!

WHAT YOU WANT IS SOMETHIN' WITHOUT ALL OF THOSE NASTY SHARP CLAWS, DOC. SOME-THING TENDER AN' JUICY.
LIKE... UH, LIKE...

DUCK %$$@!!!
NOW JUST A--

DAT DAFFY-- HE'S GOT A LOT TO LOIN ABOUT THE RESTAURANT BUSINESS!
AAAAA!!!
THAT'S ALL, FOLKS!

THE INSULT THAT MADE A BOAR OUT OF PORKY
WB1649

Writer: M.Eury Pencils: D.Alvarez Inks: M.DeCarlo Letters: J.Costanza Colors: D.Tanguay Edits: D. Kurtin

HEY! QU-QUI-QU...STOP KICKING SAND IN OUR FACES!
THAT MOBSTER IS THE WORST NUISANCE ON THE BEACH.

I'D FILL YA FULLA LEAD-- ONLY YOU'RE SO PORKY YA MIGHT LAND ON ME AN' FLATTEN ME.

THE LITTLE JE-JER-JE... BULLY! I'LL GET EVEN SOME DAY.
OH, DON'T LET IT BOTHER YOU, HEFTY BOY!

BL-BLA...DARN IT! I'M SICK AND TIRED OF BEING A PUDGEPOT! CRUSHER SAYS HE CAN GIVE ME A REAL BODY. ALL RIGHT! I'LL GAMBLE MY LIFE SAVINGS AND GET HIS PAMPH-PAMPH ...BOOK!

BOY! WHAT A HU-HUN... STUDMUFFIN! THAT HOODLUM WON'T SHOVE ME AROUND AGAIN!
LATER...

YOU can be as DENSE as
CRUSHER!
Da Woild's Most Marginally Developed Man
Crusher

WHAT?! YOU HERE AGAIN? HERE'S SOME-SOMETH... A PUNCH I OWE YOU!

OH, PORKY! YOU'RE SUCH A BOAR!
HAM OF THE BEACH!
HE TAKES THE BACON!
OTHER MEN ARE PIGS!

DON'T DELAY! BE A REAL PIG TODAY!

CRUSHER'S HE-MAN METHOD, Dept. MO-RON
Looney Institute,Burbank,CA

Writers: Sean Carolan & Jenn Moore Pencils: Alvarez Inks: DeCarlo Letters: Costanza Colors: Tanguay Assists: Richards Edits: Kurtin

NAW, BOY! YER GOIN' ABOUT IT ALL WRONG! THAT'S NOT HOW YA BUILD SOMETHIN'! LEMME SHOW YA HOW IT'S DONE!

AH DO DECLARE, MISS VELVET, YOUR MINT JULEPS PACK QUITE A WALLOP...
C'MON, VALUE MEAL, LET'S GO.

HUH?
STOMP!

OH, A WISE GUY, HUH? LISSEN, NIMROD-- I'M A CHICKEN HAWK. HE'S A CHICKEN. CHICKEN HAWKS EAT CHICKENS.
SO I'M SUPER-SIZIN' WITH EXTRA-CRISPY HERE AND NO ONE'S GETTIN' IN MY WAY. CAPICE?

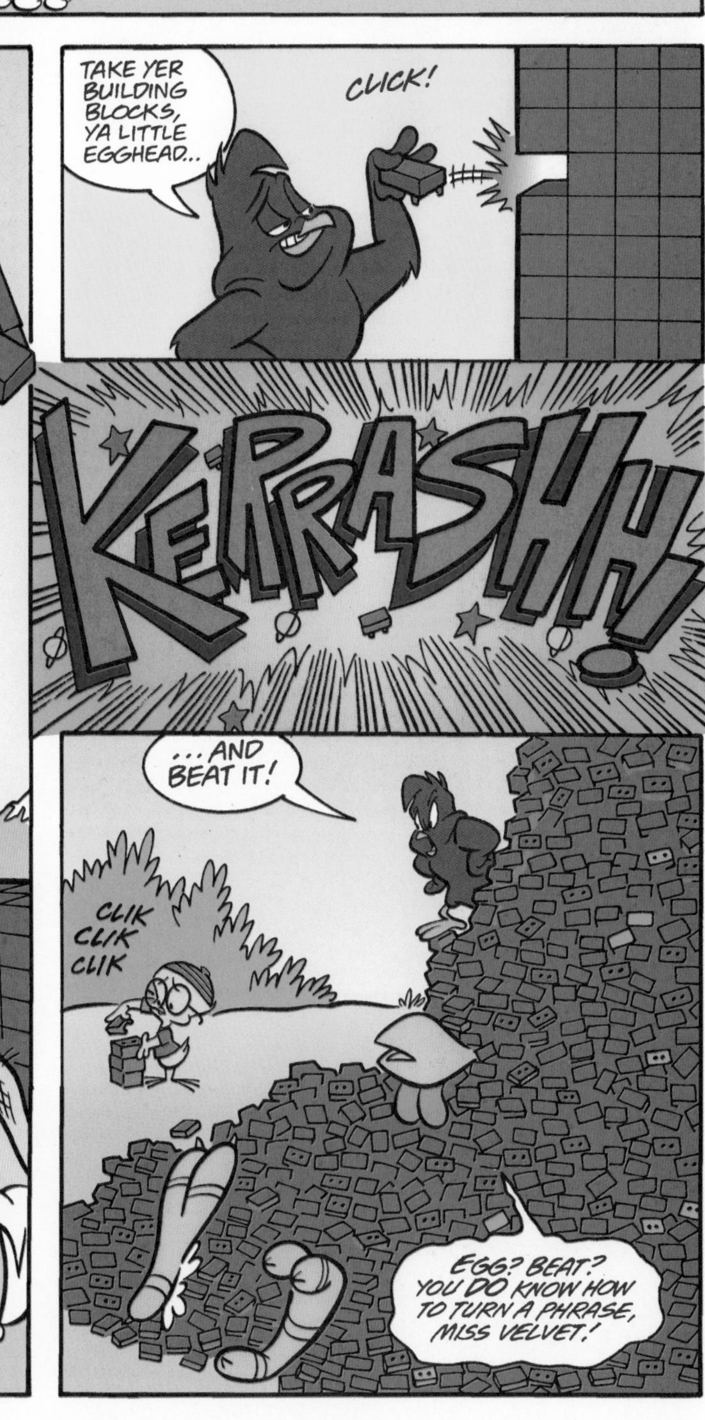
TAKE YER BUILDING BLOCKS, YA LITTLE EGGHEAD...
CLICK!
KERRASHH!
...AND BEAT IT!
CLIK CLIK CLIK
EGG? BEAT? YOU DO KNOW HOW TO TURN A PHRASE, MISS VELVET!

AH SAY, MAYBE YOU MIGHT CONSIDER EATIN' SOMETHING MORE BITE-SIZED, BOY.
BZZZZZZZ

BZZZZZZ
SEEMS TO ME A FIELD MOUSE'D FIT BETTER IN THAT PINT-SIZED PIE-HOLE O'
LISTEN, HORS D'OEUVRE, I MAY BE TINY, BUT I GOT ME A ECONO-SIZE APPETITE!

WHAT THE HECK...?
SHEESH... ENOUGH WITH THE TWO-BIT BARNSTORMING, ALREADY!
TWANNG!
KRAK

AWW, AIN'T THAT THE CUTEST THING -- THE LI'L EGGHEAD EVEN BUILT A LI'L COCKPIT, WITH A LI'L CONTROL PANEL, AN' A LI'L BLINKY SELF-DESTRUCT BUTTON--
WHAT IS IT, BOY? YOU TRYIN' TA TELL ME SOMETHIN'? SPEAK UP!

KRA-BOOM!
LET'S GO, BRAIN FOOD--OR BY THE TIME I TUCK IN THERE'LL BE NOTHIN' LEFT BUT CHICKEN JERKY!
AH SIMPLY MUST HAVE YO' RECIPE FOR COQUILLE ST. JACQUES, MISS VELVET...

EASE UP NOW, BOY! AH SAY, HAVE YOU EVAH CONSIDERED THE OTHER WHITE MEAT?
LAUGH IT UP, POT PIE...

WAITAMINNIT...
HOT SPIT ON A GRIDDLE, IT'S THE MOTHER LOAD!

SO LONG, SHRIMPY! I'M OFF TO BAG MOBY CHICK!
SHRIMPY? SIZE, I SAY, SIZE ISN'T EVERYTHING, BOY!
CRASH!
CLATTER
CLATTER!

GOOD GOIN', SON! LOOKS, I SAY, LOOKS LIKE THAT CHICKEN HAWK FELL FOR YOUR LITTLE TRICK --LOCK, BLOCK AN' BARREL!
THAT'S A JOKE, SON! LOCK, BLOCK AND BARREL! GET IT?

NICE BOY, BUT ABOUT AS BRIGHT AS A BROOM CLOSET...!
THAT'S ALL FOLKS!

HI, AND WELCOME TO ANOTHER "MOVIE MINUTE." I'M LEONARD MOLTEN...
MOVIE MINUTE
ME TAZ.
WB1684

TONIGHT, WE'LL BE REVIEWING "ARMAGEDDON OUTTA HERE" --
--STARRING BRUCE KILLUS, LIV TAYLOR AND BENNY FLECK.
TAZ LIKE DANCING CANDY AD.

I FELT THIS WAS A CLOYING, MELO-DRAMATIC STAB AT AN "EVENT" MOVIE WITH PAPER-THIN CHARACTERS AND AN EVEN THINNER PLOT. SPEAKING AS A FILMATIC EXPERT GENIUS, I HATED IT.
TAZ FEEL LIV BOTH RADIANT AND POIGNANT AS EMBODIMENT OF FRAILTY OF LIFE! TAZ LIKE! TAZ CRY! TAZ CALL MOM AFTER MOVIE!

DID WE WATCH THE SAME MOVIE?!? THAT OVER-LIPPED GANGLY WAIF WAS TERRIBLE!
NO SPEAK BAD ABOUT FUTURE MRS. TAZ!

CHOMP!

AND THAT'S IT FOR THIS WEEK. NEXT WEEK, WE'LL BE REVIEWING "MEET JOE'S BACK."
TAZ LIKING ALREADY! Belch! BYE BYE!
THAT'S ALL FOLKS!

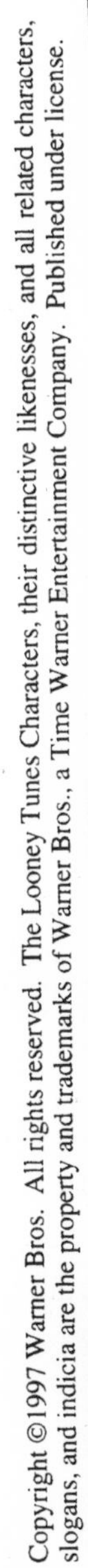

Writer: Dana Kurtin Penciler: Pablo Zamboni Inker: Scott McRae Letterer: Bob Pinaha Colorist: Tom Zuiko

One day, Widdle Wed Widing Tweety was fwying thwough the woods on the way to Gwanny's house. "Beware the Big Bad Puddy Tat", Gwanny told him. "He'll try to catch and eat you!" "Okay, Gwanny," said Widdle Wed Widing Tweety.

But at Gwanny's house, Gwanny was nowhere to be found! "Yoo hoo," said Widdle Wed Widing Tweety. "Gwanny, are you home?" "I'm in here", said a gwuff voice.

Widdle Wed Widing Tweety was very wowwied to see Gwanny sick in bed! "Why, Gwanny," said Tweety, "You don't wook at all well! Your widdle voice sounds wough and harsh! Pwus, you've gwown a mustache!" "Come closer, my dear", said Gwanny.

"Why, Gwanny, what big eyes you have," said Widdle Wed Widing Tweety.
"The better to see you with, my dear," said Gwanny.

"Why, Gwanny, what big ears you have," said Widdle Wed Widing Tweety.
"The better to hear you with, my dear," said Gwanny.

"Why, Gwanny, what big teeth you have," said Widdle Wed Widding Tweety.
Gwanny smiled. "The better to..."

"...Eat you with, my dear," said the Big Bad Puddy Tat! And with that, he ate Widdle Wed Widing Tweety in one gulp!

I LOVE HAPPY ENDINGS! TIME FOR LUNCH!
WAIT, PUDDY! WE'RE NOT DONE!

WHADDAYA MEAN, NOT DONE? THE CAT ATE THE BIRD! WHAT ELSTHE COULD POSSIBLY HAPPEN?
WET ME FINISH!

Now Widdle Wed Widing Tweety sat in the Bad Puddy's dark, stinky stomach. "Pee-yew," said Tweety. "I don't wike it in here at all!"

So Widdle Wed Widing Tweety began to hop and weap and do cawisthenics. He gave that big bad ol' puddy tat the biggest, baddest, Puddy-Tattiest stomachache that bad ol' puddy tat had ever had!

The Big Bad Puddy Tat spit Widdle Wed Widing Tweety wight out! "What's the big idea?" spluttered the Puddy Tat. "Stay still already!"

Widdle Wed Widing Tweety said to the Big Bad Puddy, "You ate me so fast, I didn't have time to give you your pwesent!"
"A pwesent?" said the Puddy. "For me? What is it?"

"A gweat big mawwet to hit you with," said Wittle Wed Widing Tweety.

LEMME SEE THAT! THAT'S RIDICULOUSTH! WHERE IN THISTH BOOK DOES IT SAY A LITTLE BIRD WHACKED A GREAT BIG PUDDY TAT WITH A MALLET?
WIGHT HERE!
WHAM
I JUST WOVE HAPPY ENDINGS, DON'T YOU?
The End

TRAMPOLINED UNDERFOOT
writers: J. MOORE & S. CAROLAN
pencils: DAVID ALVAREZ
inks: MIKE DeCARLO
letters: JOHN COSTANZA
colors: DAVID TANGUAY
assists: HARVEY RICHARDS
edits: DANA KURTIN
WB1694
LUNCH
(GOTCHA)
ME
TRAMPOLINE
HEH HEH!

MEEP MEEP!
!
POING POING

POING POING!

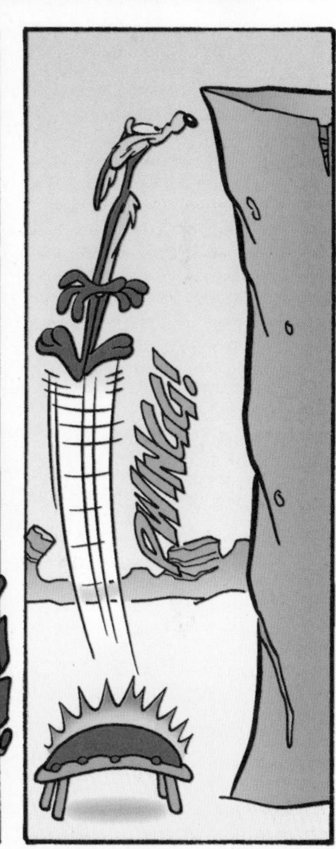
PWINGG!

WUMP!

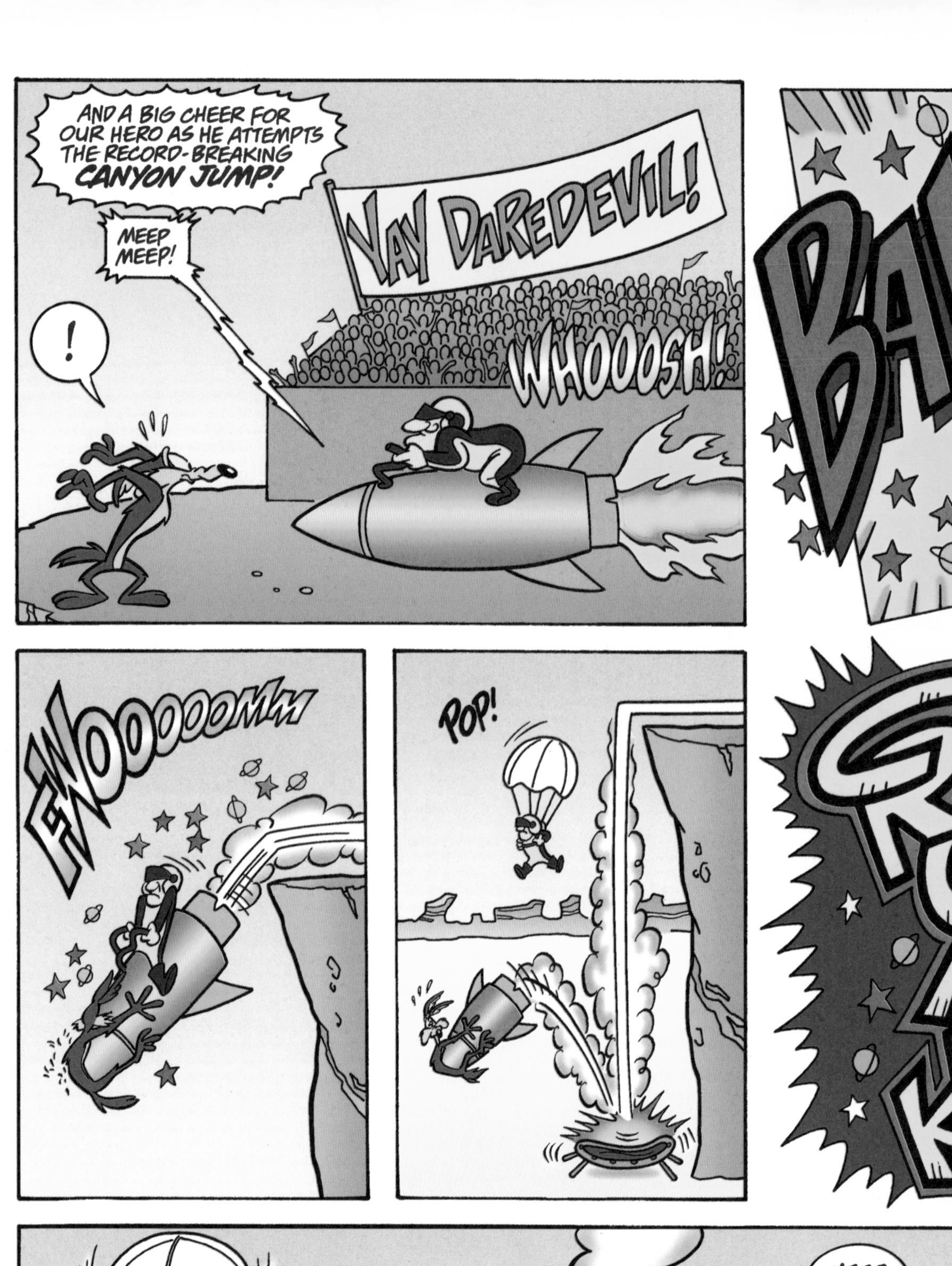
AND A BIG CHEER FOR OUR HERO AS HE ATTEMPTS THE RECORD-BREAKING CANYON JUMP!
MEEP MEEP!
YAY DAREDEVIL!
!
WHOOOSH!
BAM!
FWOOOOOMM
POP!
CRUNNK!

MEEP MEEP!
THAT'S ALL FOLKS

CLICK!
FLASH!
CLICK!
BOWLING
TOURNAMENT
TODAY
STRIKE 'EM OUT SAM
MAKE SURE YA SNAP MY GOOD SIDE, BOYS--
--CUZ STRIKE 'EM OUT SAM'S THE ROUGHEST, TOUGHEST, STRIKE ROLLING-EST HOMBRE EVER TO PICK UP A SEVEN-TEN SPLIT!

FWASH
HEY!
THUMP THUMP THUMP

BOWLING
AHH, ME ANTIQUE CARROT COLLECTION LOOKS GOOD ENOUGH TO EAT!
B. BUNNY
THUMP
THUMP
THUMP

WB1719
THUMP
SMASH
CRASH!
IN FACT, I'D SAY SMASHING.
TEN PIN ALLEY
WRITER: BILL MATTHENY
PENCILS: DAVID ALVAREZ
INKS: MIKE DeCARLO
LETTERS: JOHN COSTANZA
COLORS: DAVE TANGUAY
ASSISTS: HARVEY RICHARDS
EDITS: DANA KURTIN & HEIDI MacDONALD

ME STONE-AGED BEAUTY! RUBBLE!

GIMME BACK MY BOWLING BALL, YA LONG-EARED VARMINT!
DO YOU KNOW WHO AH AM?
SOME MA-ROON CAN'T TELL THE DIFFERENCE BETWEEN A BACK ALLEY AND A BOWLING ALLEY?

YOU JUST PUT THE KIBOSH ON ME ANTIQUE CARROT COLLECTION! WHADDAYA GOING TO DO ABOUT IT?
NOTHIN'--

--EXCEPT BLAST YA IF YOU DON'T STOP FLAPPING YER TRAP!
YIKES!

OF COURSE, YOU REALIZE THAT THIS MEANS WAR!

ALL RIGHT! I WANTS TO BOWL AND I WANTS TO BOWL NOW! WHO'S FIRST?
YOO HOO, MR. STRIKE 'EM OUT SAM!!! I'LL BOWL A GAME WITH YA!

START BOWLING, YA LONG-EARED GALOOT!
OH GOODIE! I CAN PRACTICE ME BOOMERANG BALL. I LOINED IT IN AUSTRALIA.

HA, HA! NICE TRY, RABBIT, BUT YA COULDN'T HIT THE BROADSIDE OF A KANGAROO!
DO YA THINK SO, DOC?
WHACK!

LUCKY ME. I GOT A STRIKE!
WHAM!
THUMP
THUMP
OHHH!!!

HURRY UP!
JUST REMOVING LINT FROM THE ALLEY. Heh, heh, heh. AIN'T I A STINKER?
OIL

STAND BACK, RABBIT! AHM A-SCATTERING THOSE PINS!
OKAY! MAYBE I CAN LOIN A THING OR TWO FROM WATCHING DA MASTER.

OH, IS THAT WHAT DEY MEAN BY "PUTTING YER BODY INTO YER SWING"?
WHOA! YIKES! HOO BOY!
OIL
WHOOSH!

WHAMM!

CRUNCH! CRUNCH! YOU WERE RIGHT, DOC. YOU GOT A STRIKE, TOO!
MUMBLE-- PESKY VARMINT.

WHEN I GETS MY HANDS ON THAT RABBIT, AHM A-GONNA SHAVE HIS GIZZARD AND TAN HIS HIDE!

UNGH! I BETTER TAKE MY TOIN NOW. OL' SAM'LL HAVE ANUDDER HISSY FIT IF I KEEP 'EM WAITING!

MOTHER!

CRASH!
EH, I THOUGHT I'D SEE YA AROUND, DOC, BUT NOT DIS ROUND!
HARDY HAR HAR, VARMINT!

THAT DOES IT, RABBIT! NO MORE MR. NICE GUY!
WHY, SAM, YOU LOOK A BIT ON DA TESTY SIDE. IMAGINE THAT!

Ahm a-settlin' this score right now! STICK 'EM UP!
BLAM BLAM
OKAY, OKAY! DON'T GET YOUR SIX-GUNS IN A KNOT!

OF ALL THE CRITTERS IN ALL THE BOWLING ALLEYS IN ALL THE WORLD, I HAD TA RUN INTO THIS ONE!
YEAH, AIN'T YOU THE LUCKY ONE?

CRUNCH!

EH, WHAT WERE YA SAYIN', DOC?
AH HATE THAT RABBIT.

HEH, HEH, HEH. SAY YER PRAYERS, YA FUR-COVERED FLEABAG!
ONCE YUH STICK YER FINGERS INTO THIS HERE BOMB, YER RABBIT RAGOUT!
GLUE

HERE YUH GO, RABBIT! I GOTCHA A BRAND-NEW BOWLING BALL JUST TO SHOW THERE'S NO HARD FEELINGS!
FOR ME? WHY, SAM! YA SHOULDN'T HAVE!
I CAN'T WAIT TO USE IT!
FSSST

WAIT A MINUTE! THAT AIN'T HOW YUH HOLD A BOWLING BALL!
FSSST
LET ME SHOW YA HOW, YA HARE-BRAINED HALFWIT!
OH, WOULD YOU?

YA GOTTA PUT YOUR FINGERS IN HERE JUST LIKE THIS!
COULD YOU SPEAK SLOWER WHILE I COPY DIS DOWN, DOC?
FSSST

THEN YUH HAUL BACK...
OH, THEN WHAT?
FSSST

...AND LET 'ER--
RIP?!?
I SEE. I THINK I'VE GOT IT NOW, DOC!
NOT AS GOOD AS YOU'RE GONNA GET IT, THOUGH.
FSSST!
ULP.
WHOOOSH
KA-
BLAM!
CARRY DA SEVEN, TIMES DA SQUARE ROOT OF 84?
WELL, WHADDAYA KNOW, SAM? I WON!
EH, ANYBODY UP FOR A GAME?
THAT'S ALL FOLKS!

THE AMAZON BASIN. THE MOST UNFORGIVING ENVIRONMENT ON EARTH. MOSTLY UNEXPLORED...

...FOR NO MAN HAS VENTURED INTO THIS BEAUTIFUL BUT DEADLY PARADISE AND LIVED TO TELL THE TALE. BUT WHERE MAN HAS FAILED...
WBTK 1763

...A BUNNY MAY TRIUMPH!
Lola Bunny and the
TEMPLE OF Thetzalatlhui
FOR THE LAST TIME, I DO NOT HAVE SPARE CHANGE!
SNARL!
STORY: SEAN CAROLAN & JENNIFER MOORE
PENCILS: STEPHANIE GLADDEN
INKS: MIKE DeCARLO
LETTERS: JOHN COSTANZA
COLORS: DAVE TANGUAY
ASSTS: HARVEY RICHARDS
EDITS: HEIDI MacDONALD

THWAK!

GET A JOB LIKE THE REST OF US, SLACKER!!

ALL THIS "DANK" CANNOT BE GOOD FOR MY PORES...
Who dares defile the temple of Thetzalatlhui?!?

MACHU PIZZA DELIVERY!
have you... the crazy bread?
OF COURSE!
YAY! PIZZA!

IT'S A LOUSY ROUTE... BUT THE TIPS ARE GREAT!
THAT'S ALL FOLKS!

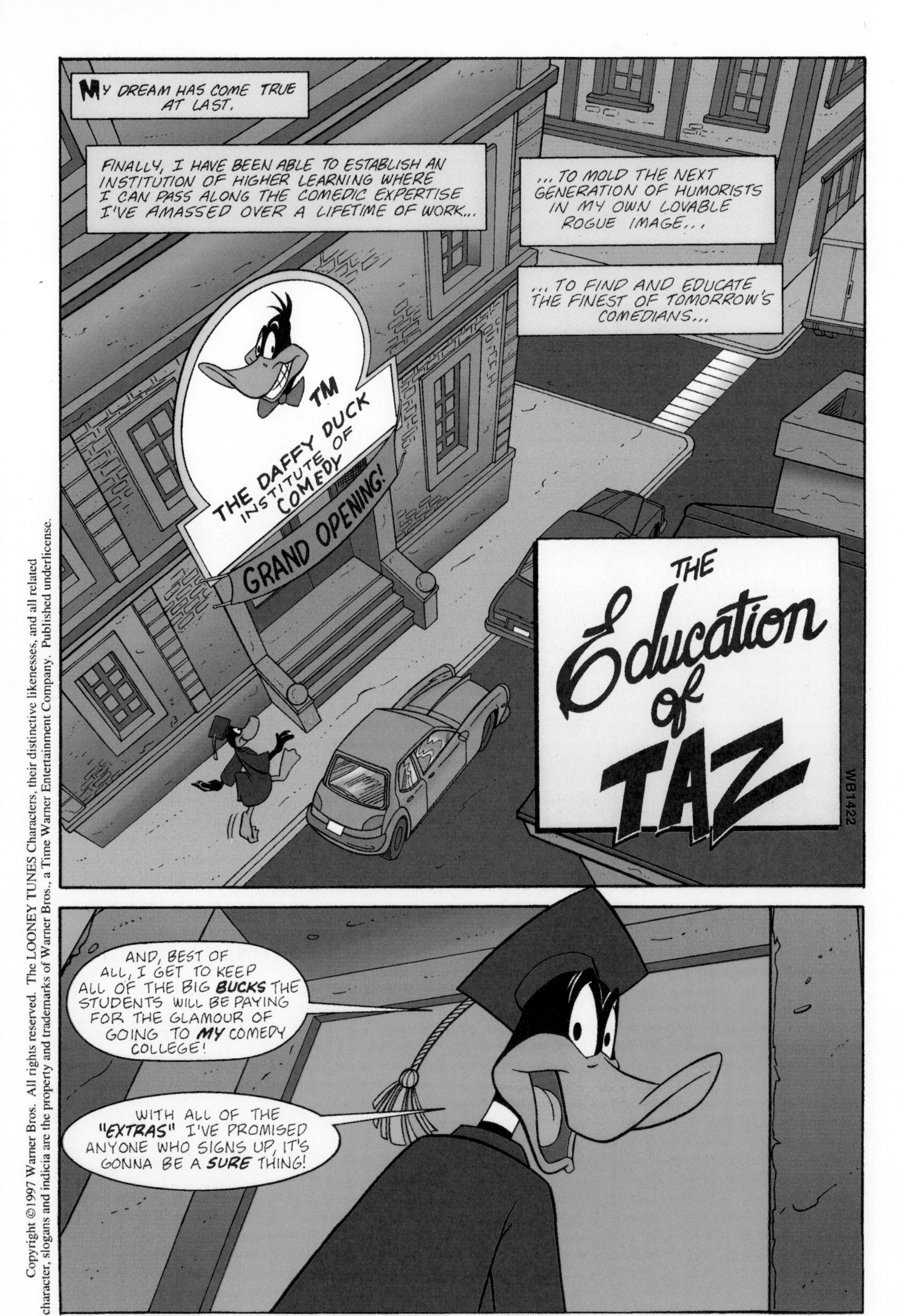

Writer:Terry Collins Penciller: Nelson Luty Inker: Jim Amash Letterer: Teresa Davidson Colorist: Jahrome Youngker

WONDER WHERE ALL OF MY NEW STUDENTS ARE **HIDING?**
GUESS THEY MUST ALREADY BE IN CLASS--READY TO SIP FROM THE CUP OF MY COMEDY GENIUS!
EXIT

GREETINGS, ASPIRING THESPIANS! I AM **PROFESSOR DUCK**--YOUR MENTOR FOR THE NEXT FEW YEARS!
I CAN'T TELL YOU HOW HAPPY I AM TO SEE SO MANY EAGER YOUNG--

--FACES?
GOOD MORNING, **TEECH-CHUR.**
CRUNCH
CRUNCH

=COFF= =COFF= **TAZ** THIRSTY. GO GET DRINK OF **WADDAH.**
YES, OF COURSE. IN FACT, I THINK I'LL JOIN YOU.

WELL, YOU'RE THE **REGISTRAR**--YOU TELL ME! WHERE ARE ALL THE EAGER YOUNG FACES WITH THEIR EXTRA THICK **BANK ACCOUNTS?**
IT'S A NEW SCHOOL, DAFFY. IT TAKES TIME TO BUILD **ENROLLMENT.** FOR NOW, THAT **TASMANIAN DEVIL** IS YOUR **LONE** PUPIL--

--AND HE'S AN **EXCHANGE STUDENT,** SO YOU'D BETTER MAKE THE BEST OF IT!
--BECAUSE WITHOUT STUDENTS, YOU LOSE YOUR **ACCREDITATION** AND THE COLLEGE BOARD **CLOSES** YOUR FACILITY DOWN. UNDERSTAND?
YES=GULP= SIR.

AND WHAT BRINGS YOU HERE, BIG FELLA? YOU WANT TO GO INTO STAND-UP? TELEVISION? THE CIRCUS?
TAZ LIKE WAFFLES!
CHACK
WAFFLE IRON

OH, THE FREE WAFFLE IRON ROPED YOU IN, eh? WELL, YOU'LL GET YOUR TICKET TO DINING PLEASURE UPON GRADUATION.
GRAT YOU WAIT SHUN?
NEVER MIND. LET'S SEE HOW WELL YOU READ FROM A SCRIPT.

Ahem. TOP OF PAGE FORTY-THREE. MY LINE IS, "SHOOT THE DUCK! SHOOT 'EM! SHOOT 'EM!"
?
TAZ GOT NO GUN. WANT WAFFLE. AND SYRUP.
DUCK! RABBIT! DUCK!

SHEESH, YOU DUMB FURBALL-- THAT'S NOT YOUR LINE! READ YOUR LINE!
DON'T JUST STAND THERE BLINKING LIKE AN IMBECILE--DO SOMETHING!
CHOMP

HEY! YOU'RE DESTROYING SCHOOL PROPERTY! THAT'S MONEY OUTTA MY POCKET!
SMACK
CHEW
GRIND
MUNCH

WHAT DO YOU HAVE TO SAY FOR YOURSELF, NOW, GENIUS?
URP!
PAPER GOOD. TAZ LIKE WAFFLE BETTER.

OKAY, SO YOU LIKE TO AD-LIB. AN IMPROV MAN, UNFETTERED BY THE WRITTEN WORD.
WELL, TWO CAN PLAY AT THAT DISCIPLINE, GRASSHOPPER! I'M THE TEACHER-- YOU'RE THE STUDENT, CAPEESH?!

THERE, BAGGY-EYES-- ONE HAT WITH EAR FLAPS AND ONE POP GUN! YOU HAPPY?
NOW FOLLOW MY LEAD--AND TRY TO KEEP UP, hmmmm?
POF

Eh, WHAT'S UP, DOC?
Ehh? DUCK GO AWAY? NOW BUNNY?
Daffy Duck

YEAH, RIGHT-- I'M A BUNNY. WELL, GO AHEAD, MISTER COMEDY GENIUS! WHAT'S YOUR FIRST IMPULSE?
COME ON, LET'S HAVE IT! PULL THE TRIGGER ON YOUR NEXT WONDERFUL INSULT!

BAD IMPULSE! BAD!
TAZ LIKE BUNNY! TAZ EAT BUNNY!
GET WAFFLE NOW?

OBVIOUSLY, VERBAL REPARTEE ISN'T YOUR GAME.
ACK! @$&#! TAZ STILL HUNGRY!

LUNCHTIME COMES LATER. LET'S TRY SOME BASIC MIME EXERCISES.
I'LL SAY A WORD AND YOU ACT OUT YOUR INTERPRETATION, OKAY?

HAPPY!

CORNCOB! SHOEHORN!

TOOTHBRUSH! PADLOCK! LOBOTOMY!

Um... WAFFLES?
WAH-FULLLS!?

NO! NO WAFFLES! I TAKE IT BACK-- I TAKE IT BACCCCK!!
WHERE WAFFLES? WHERE!?

ANYONE EVER POINT OUT THAT YOU, SIR, HAVE A ONE-TRACK MIND?
Mmmmmm! TAZ LIKE WAFFLES!

KIDS TODAY! NO SUBTLETY! YOU WANT IT BIGGER THAN LIFE--YOU GOT IT!
WHAT YOU NEED IS A GROUNDING IN GOOD OL' FASHIONED SLAPSTICK!

BACK TO THE BASICS, THAT'S MY EDUCATIONAL MOTTO!
I BELIEVE SIGHT GAGS ARE UNIQUELY SUITED TO YOUR OWN HIGH-ENERGY STYLE.

NOW, HOLD THIS AND DON'T DO ANYTHING UNTIL I GIVE THE WORD.

OKAY, THROW THE PIE AND HIT THE TARGET RIGHT ON THE OL' KISSER!
GO AHEAD, LET 'ER RIP!

ANY DAY NOW...

SLURRRP! MMM! TAZ LIKE PIE!
WHY AM I NOT SURPRISED?

OKAY, LET'S TRY AGAIN. WHEN I GIVE THE **SIGNAL,** YOU THROW THE PIE.
WHY TAZ THROW PIE? TAZ LIKE PIE! TAZ *EAT* PIE!

NO! NO LIKE! **NO EAT!**
YOU THROW THE PIE BECAUSE I SAID SO! A CREAM PIE IN THE SNOOT IS **HILARIOUS!** OKAY!?

NOW, WAIT UNTIL I GIVE THE HIGH SIGN AND--
CHOMP! SLURP! GULP!

YOU ATE IT, DIDN'T YOU?
Uh-huh.

THIS TIME, I'M NOT TURNING MY BACK ON YOU! NOW, TAKE THE PIE AND THROW IT!
OKAY.

NO! NO! NOT LIKE THAT-- LIKE THIS, YOU **BRAIN-DAMAGED** WAD OF HAIR!
SPLOOT

Heh-heh-heh
STOP IT! STOP LAUGHING! THIS ISN'T AMUSING!

YOU DON'T HAVE A FUNNY BONE IN YOUR ENTIRE BODY--UNLESS IT BELONGS TO SOME POOR UNLUCKY SLOB YOU GOBBLED UP!
WHY ARE YOU HERE, hah? WHY DID YOU COME TO TORMENT ME?

TAZ LIKE WAFFLES!
"TAZ LIKE WAFFLES!" SO WHAT? EVERYBODY LIKES WAFFLES, YOU MORON!

SAY, THAT'S NOT BAD! MAYBE THAT PEABRAIN OF YOURS IS SHARPER THAN I THOUGHT!

TM
DAFFY DUCK'S BREAKFAST PALACE
GRAND OPENING!
PLENTY FOR EVERYBODY, JUST TAKE A SEAT!

HEY, I HAD TO DO SOMETHING WITH ALL THOSE WAFFLE IRONS!
SYRUP
That's All, Folks!

SILENCE IS GOLDEN
WB1757
WRITER: BRETT KOTH PENCILS: DAVID ALVAREZ
INKS: MIKE DeCARLO LETTERS: JOHN COSTANZA
COLORS: DAVID TANGUAY ASSISTS: HARVEY RICHARDS
EDITS: HEIDI MacDONALD

I'M SORRY... WHAT WERE YOU SAYING?

OH, NOTHING.
THAT'S ALL FOLKS!